The British Natural History Collection

Volume 2

OTTERS

OTTERS

Paul Chanin

Illustrations by Guy Troughton

Whittet Books

Whittet Books Ltd
1 St John's Lane
Stansted
Essex CM24 8JU
mail@whittetbooks.com
www.whittetbooks.com

First published 1993 *(in the British Natural History Series)*
This revised second edition 2013
Text © Paul Chanin 1993, 2013
Illustrations © Guy Troughton 1993
Otters painting © Guy Troughton 2013
Photographs © Laurie Campbell 2013

A catalogue record for this publication is available from the
British Library.

ISBN 978 1 873580 84 4

Designed by Lodge Graphics

CONTENTS

The photographs are between pages 74 and 75.

ACKNOWLEDGEMENTS

The first edition of this book (published in the *British Natural History Series*) owed much to the research that had been carried out by Hans Kruuk and his team at the Banchory Research Station in Scotland and I paid tribute to them then. This one does too, but I have also been able to draw on the work of many other fine ecologists studying otters in Britain and elsewhere in Europe. The considerable amount of new information that has been gleaned is largely responsible for the fact that this edition is somewhat longer than the first.

New technologies, such as DNA fingerprinting, have led to some fascinating new insights into otter biology. So has good old-fashioned fieldwork involving the recording of spraints, and I have been able to report three more national surveys in the UK showing how the otter population is recovering from the catastrophic decline of the last century. Another well-established technique that has led to some intriguing discoveries is the post-mortem. Many unexpected observations have come from the meticulous work of Vic Simpson and his colleagues.

I would again like to express my special thanks to Sam Erlinge, who guided my early interests and Don Jefferies with whom I collaborated for many years.

Special mention must be made of my good friend and colleague, Jim Conroy who died in March 2011. I had some unforgettable experiences doing otter surveys with Jim in Shetland, as well as enjoying field work and meetings in other parts of Europe as members of the IUCN Otter Specialist Group. We spent many happy hours discussing otter ecology, the politics of otter conservation and his view that Scotland was 'God's Own Country' (despite its southern neighbours).

Jim chaired the OSG for several years during which time he did a great deal not only to foster otter conservation internationally, but also to inspire and encourage the next generation of ecologists. We all miss him a great deal. He made a major contribution to the first edition of this book by reading and commenting on it and now it is hard to know who to turn to for informed, but informal, friendly advice and guidance.

I am also grateful to other colleagues in the Otter Specialist Group who, for the most part, are responsible for the work reported here and whose lively discussions on the OSG email forum add greatly to the interest and enjoyment of working with otters. There is also a loose network of people involved in otter conservation in the UK, many of whom used to work for the Otters and Rivers Project or related organisations. I have learned a great deal, informally, from many of these people and would particularly like to pay tribute to James Williams, another careful observer, as well as a source of interesting and original ideas.

Don and Jim kindly read the first edition for me as did Su Hiscox. Laura Bonesi has contributed greatly to this edition by reading it in draft, and her thoughtful and helpful comments have considerably improved it. However, I suspect that, with Italian as her first language, she is still puzzled as to why the plural of mink is mink and not minks! As ever, mistakes and obscurities are the responsibility of the author.

The loss of Annabel Whittet who devised the original series and published it for many years is a sad one. I shall always remember her calm, patient voice reassuring me that she was not pressing me for the manuscript, just wondering how I was getting on. Shirley Greenall has taken up this mantle and continues the approach, for which I am very grateful.

Finally, the book is longer and so is the list of dedications. This one is for Sarah, Victoria and Taran.

PREFACE

In August 2011, the Environment Agency announced that otters had returned to Kent, the last of the English counties to be recolonised by them in their recovery from near extinction in England last century. A conservation success story, and one for which the Environment Agency (and its antecedent, the Nation Rivers Authority) can take some credit.

Many other organisations have played their part although, to my mind, the unsung heroes of the story are the members of the Toxic Chemicals and Wildlife Division at Monks Wood Experimental Station. They investigated the links between new 'improved' pesticides first used in the 1950s and massive kills and major declines of many predatory species of birds in the UK. It was their work which led to a reduction in use and finally to a ban on these substances. I was lucky enough to work there for a few months in what would now be called my Gap Year.

When the first edition of this book was published I wrote that we were waiting for the results of the third Survey of otters in England. They were announced not long after, and were certainly encouraging. In the 1970s, only six per cent of sites searched had had signs of otters present but by the third survey, in the early 1990s, it had reached nearly twenty-five per cent. The most recent (fifth) survey completed in 2010 showed a further increase and that both numbers and range continue to grow.

There are many interesting lessons to be learned from the 'Decline and Recovery' of otters. The most obvious is not to spread new chemicals throughout the environment until you thoroughly understand their effects. One, sadly, we don't seem to have learned yet. For me, a more personal one is the time scale involved. More or less one human lifetime from the start of the decline to (we hope) recovery – my lifetime.

The pesticides which caused the problem were first introduced just as I started primary school. Twelve years later when I took my A levels the decline was well under way and the otter hunts were collecting information which provided the first conclusive evidence of this. Ten years after this the population was close to extinction in England and my career was starting. The first national otter surveys began that year and Don Jefferies and I obtained evidence which pointed firmly towards the otter being another species affected by those pesticides.

Now, Don is retired, I am approaching the end of my working life, and otters are about two-thirds of their way along the road to recovery. On the basis of the first two sets of national surveys Don predicted the course of recovery. Subsequent surveys of England, especially the fourth, have shown a certain amount of lagging behind this, though otters seem to have been making up time since. If all goes well, by my eightieth year otters will be found at about eighty per cent of the sites searched – if the surveys still continue. I live in hope of seeing both!

Another cycle of change which has happened in my lifetime is in attitudes to predatory animals in general and otters in particular. In the early 1950s otters were still considered to be pests, to the extent that an enquiry into otter hunting considered that it was still important to control them. Later, public affection for otters was greatly influenced by Gavin Maxwell's book *Ring of Bright Water* and the subsequent film. Today, birds of prey as well as carnivorous mammals are regarded much more highly, due in no small part to the influence of television.

Even so, as the otter becomes widespread in Britain once more, rather than a rare and threatened species, it is coming into conflict with the interests of some people. In the past, salmon and trout fishermen were particularly incensed by the fact that otters ate some of 'their' fish. Today it is the coarse fishing fraternity, particularly those who pursue trophy specimens, who would rather that this charming and elusive animal had remained as scarce as it was last century. Clearly there are some benefits in scarcity!

In this book I have tried to tell various otter stories: about their feeding and breeding habits, their social behaviour, relationships with man and, of course, about the decline and recovery. Like all animals, the more you find out about them, the more fascinating they become. We have learned a great deal about otters over my life time but there is a lot more to learn and plenty of scope for another generation of ecologists to find out more. I envy them!

Paul Chanin, 2013

WHAT ARE OTTERS?

Otters are members of the weasel family, the Mustelidae, one of several families belonging to a group of mammals known as the Carnivora which includes wolves, dogs and foxes, bears, raccoons, pandas, cats, hyaenas, civets, genets and mongooses. Carnivores are typically meat eaters with sharp canine teeth for killing and holding their prey and sharp-edged slicing cheek teeth for cutting up its flesh. On the other hand their skeletons tend not to be very specialised as many of them have to be very adaptable. Some can run quite quickly but also climb trees. Others need to be able to knock over or hold down struggling prey with their paws as well as run fast enough to catch it. The design of a carnivore's body is often more of a compromise than, for example, a gazelle whose legs are highly adapted to running fast, or a gibbon whose long arms are beautifully designed for swinging through trees.

Mustelids fit this pattern rather well. They have long, thin bodies and short legs, ideal for pushing through dense undergrowth or hunting in tunnels for prey, and can walk on the soles of their feet, like humans, rather than on their toes like the speedier cats, dogs and hyaenas. However, typical

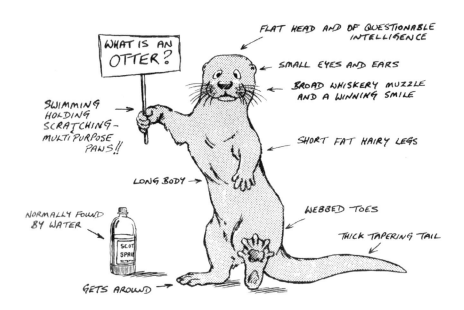

5

mustelid skulls are specialised, with an elongated cranium often topped by a narrow crest for the attachment of strong jaw muscles and sharp slicing molar teeth for turning prey into bite-sized chunks.

The Mustelidae are divided into subfamilies which include the typical weasels (including stoats, polecats, mink), martens, the wolverine, skunks, various types of badgers, the honey badger and, of course, the otters.

There are several species of otters but opinions differ as to how many. Until a few decades ago it was considered that there were eighteen or nineteen, but now it is agreed that some of these are simply different varieties of the same species. In the 1970s an American zoologist recognised only nine species which had the benefit of simplicity, but today the generally accepted number is thirteen and this is the classification I use below. Older books may use different classifications and also different scientific names.

EUROPEAN OTTERS

This is easy; there is only one, our own species *Lutra lutra*, best described as the Eurasian otter which, apart from in this chapter, is the one described in this book.

Although it is now missing from parts of its former range it still inhabits an enormous area, much greater than any other species. As the map shows,

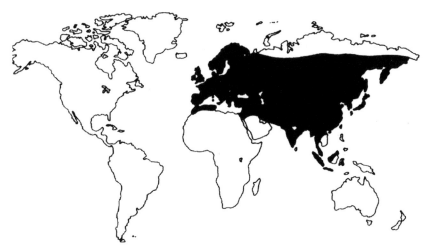

Distribution of the Eurasian otter.

its range extends from the cool damp climate of the west of Ireland to the humid tropical forests of Asia and from the hot dry lands of North Africa to the cold of northern Russia and Finland.

ASIAN OTTERS

In addition to the Eurasian otter there are three species found in Asia: the Asian (or Oriental) short-clawed (or small-clawed) otter (*Aonyx cinereus*), the smooth-coated otter (*Lutrogale perspicillata*) and the delightfully named hairy-nosed otter (*Lutra sumatrana*).

The short-clawed otter is a little smaller than the Eurasian otter (see table on page 11) and is probably one of the most familiar species since it is often kept in zoos and wildlife parks. In the wild its diet consists of crabs, molluscs, frogs and small fish and, in keeping with this diet, which includes a high proportion of hard-shelled prey, its teeth are modified to be better at crushing than slicing. Its name reflects another adaptation to feeding. The claws are reduced to a vestige with the result that the forepaws look quite hand-like. In the wild they are used for probing in the mud and feeling under stones. In captivity I have seen a tame one that was adept at juggling with hazel nuts and stealing key rings from handbags. Another characteristic of this species is its sociability. Families are large (litters of four or five are normal) and may on occasion join together so that there have been sightings of as many as fifteen in one group. It is found in South East Asia including parts of India and southern China.

The smooth-coated otter is similar in size and habits to the Eurasian otter. Little studied in the wild, it is probably best known from Gavin Maxwell's book *Ring of Bright Water* (his first otter, Mijbil, was this species). Its diet consists principally of fish although like most otters it does not disdain crabs in some areas. Smooth-coated otters have a very unusual distribution, the main part of the range covering India and South East Asia but with an isolated population in the extensive marshes around the Tigris and Euphrates on the borders of Iran and Iraq.

The hairy-nosed otter is most closely related to the Eurasian species. It is about the same size and seems to be ecologically similar. However, it is very little studied and only known from a few places. For some time it was believed to be a subspecies of the Eurasian otter but recent genetic studies suggest otherwise. Historically its range seems to have included much of South East

Asia from Thailand down through Indonesia and Malaysia. Today there is good evidence that it still occurs in southern Sumatra, southern Thailand, south-west Cambodia and south Vietnam.

AFRICAN OTTERS

South of the Sahara three species are sometimes recognised: the African clawless otter (*Aonyx capensis*) closely related to, but larger than the short-clawed otter, the Congo clawless otter (*Aonyx congicus*) and the spotted-necked otter (*Hydrictis maculicollis*).

Clawless otters have lost their front claws entirely but retain those on the middle toes of the hind foot and, like their Asian cousins, specialise on invertebrate prey rather than on fish. In coastal regions they have even been recorded as feeding on octopus. By contrast the smaller spotted-necked otter is a fish specialist.

Perhaps in connection with their diets, the two species are active at different times, the spotted-necked during the day and the clawless at dawn and dusk or at night. Both species are quite sociable and can often be seen in groups of four or five individuals. Occasionally spotted necked otters have been seen in groups as large as twenty.

Since the Congo clawless otter, living in the Congo basin, is surrounded to the north, east and south by the African clawless otter, it is not surprising that it is not considered by all to be a distinct species even though it has some minor differences in appearance. No doubt the secrets of this relationship will be revealed by studies of the genetic make-up of the two 'species'.

AMERICAN OTTERS

There are two species of otter found in North America: the sea otter (*Enhydra lutris* - see below) and the North American river otter (*Lontra canadensis*). The river otter used to be put in the same genus as the Eurasian otter *Lutra* and the two species are very similar in many aspects of their biology. However, genetic studies suggest a more distant relationship so American otters are now placed in the confusingly similar genus *Lontra*. The most obvious difference between the two is in reproduction; the America species having a very long gestation period due to a phenomenon known as delayed implantation. In this, the early stages of pregnancy, before the embryo implants in the uterine wall enabling it to obtain nutrients direct

The giant otter of South America.

from its mother's blood, are extended for several months. This phenomenon has been observed in several other mammal species including stoats, pine marten, badgers, seals and roe deer.

Central and South America also have river otters in the genus *Lontra*, two of which are very similar in size and habits to the one in North America. Apart from these, South America boasts two other distinct species: the giant otter (*Pteronura brasiliensis*), which can reach 1.8 m in length, and the sea cat or marine otter (*Lontra felina*), one of the smallest species.

The Neotropical otter (*Lontra longicaudis*) is found throughout South America apart from Chile and its range extends as far as Mexico in Central America. Here it is separated from the range of its northern relative by an arid region inhabited by neither species. Like the North American and Eurasian river otters its diet is dominated by fish.

Known locally as the Huillin, the southern river otter (*Lontra provocax*) is confined to Chile and Argentina and very little is known about it.

Giant otters are found mainly on larger rivers in northern and central South America where they live in family groups consisting of an adult male and female plus one or two litters of young. They feed primarily on fish, hunting close together in a group which helps to confuse the fish and make them easier to catch. Giant otters have been heavily hunted for fur in many parts of their former range, and are extinct in some.

Little is known of the sea cat which lives on the west coast of South America in Peru and Chile. It lives beside the sea and feeds along the shore where it concentrates on invertebrate prey although there are reports of it venturing into rivers to catch freshwater shrimps. Fish are not ignored but only form a quarter of the prey taken.

THE PACIFIC OCEAN OTTERS

Around much of the northern Pacific lives the intriguing sea otter, not to be confused with other otters that live beside the sea. Most species of otters will probably venture out to sea from time to time and several, including our own, are capable of living along the coast. While these are merely inland otters living at the seaside, the sea otter spends its entire life at sea. I could write a whole book on sea otters but unfortunately for me someone already has (see *Further Reading*) so a potted history is all that is required.

Sea otters feed mainly on invertebrates and are particularly fond of sea urchins and abalones (large, limpet-like molluscs). They are renowned for their habit of using rocks as tools, both to acquire their prey (they use them to bludgeon abalones into letting go) and as anvils on which to crack open the shells of clams and mussels. Spending their whole lives at sea and rarely, if ever, venturing onto land, they need exceptionally good waterproofing and insulation. Evolution has provided this in one of the densest fur coats known. Unfortunately their luxuriant fur very nearly led to their downfall. In the nineteenth century they were hunted almost to extinction for their pelts but have been protected since 1911 and have recovered in parts of their former range. Small populations are found off the west coast of North America, the best known being in California. In the small town of Monterey you can watch them from your hotel window or restaurant table if you book wisely. In the North Pacific they are found on the necklace of islands which connects America with Asia consisting of the Alaskan Peninsula and the Aleutian Islands as well as the Kurile Islands which link Kamchatka to Japan. Today they are well protected from exploitation but face, instead, other dangers. In March 1989 an oil spill from the super-tanker *Exxon*

Valdez is known to have killed a thousand of the five thousand sea otters inhabiting the area round Prince William Sound in Alaska. How many died unseen will never be known.

Sea otters are also vulnerable to attack from large predators such as white sharks and orcas (killer whales). In recent years sea otters have been almost eliminated from parts of their northern range by the depredations of orcas and this has given rise to some concern. One explanation for a recent increase in predation on sea otters by orcas is the human over-exploitation of other prey species, particularly fish.

No species of otters is currently considered to be critically endangered but five are endangered, two are vulnerable and there is one species about which we simply don't have enough information – described as 'data deficient' in the table below.

Otters of the world

	Range	Prey	Weight	Length	Status
Eurasian otter	Eur/Asia/Afr	Fish	8–10 kg	110–120 cm	NT
Hairy-nosed otter	SE Asia	Fish			EN
Spotted-necked otter	Africa	Fish	5–6 kg	100–110 cm	LC
American river otter	N & S America	Fish	7–9 kg	110–120 cm	LC
Neotropical otter	C & S America	Fish			DD
Southern river otter	S America	Fish			EN
Marine otter	S America	Inv.	4–5 kg	100–115 cm	EN
Smooth-coated otter	Asia	Fish	10–11 kg	110–130 cm	VU
Asian short-clawed otter	Asia	Inv.	4–5 kg	65–95 cm	VU
African clawless otter	Africa	Inv.	18–20 kg	130–150 cm	LC
Congo clawless otter	Africa	Inv.	c.20 kg	c.150 cm	LC
Giant otter	S America	Fish	26–32 kg	150–180 cm	EN
Sea otter	Pacific Ocean	Inv.	25–30 kg	130–140 cm	EN

Where possible, lengths and weights are given for males. Females are about 10% shorter and 25% lighter. For most species the tail is approximately 40% of total length except for sea otter in which it is 25%.

Status: NT = not threatened; LC = locally common; VU = vulnerable; EN = endangered; DD = data deficient.

WHERE DO OTTERS LIVE?

Otters are aquatic, or more correctly, semi-aquatic animals which means that they spend much of their time, while active, in water. They find virtually all of their food in, on or beside water and their dens are usually close to water. However, there are many different types of aquatic and waterside habitats, some of which are more suitable than others. Much depends on the availability of the resources needed to survive and breed.

Needless to say, an important resource is food but otters also have to take into consideration the need for shelter and refuge (from the weather as well as possible predators), suitable breeding sites and, of course, potential mates. So, before looking at the habitats which could be exploited in Britain, it is a good idea to consider the essential resources in a little more detail.

Food is obviously fundamental and, although otters may take other prey from time to time occasionally in substantial amounts, in most places for most of the time fish form the bulk of their food. The actual diet is described in detail later but one consequence is clear; that, although the sparkling little upland streams of Dartmoor, Wales, the Pennines and Scotland are very attractive to people, they are less beneficial to otters

Den in a grassy habitat.

because they are not very productive and do not have high densities of fish. Large, productive lowland streams provide much more food which is present throughout the year and, other things being equal, are much better habitats.

What about resting sites, refuges and dens? In fact, in areas where they are unlikely to be disturbed directly by people, otters are not very choosy about where they sleep. Males in particular seem willing to lie up in places which can hardly be described as secure. In Shetland they have been seen asleep on seashore rocks in broad daylight. Radio-tracking studies show that on some rivers otters may have very large numbers of sleeping sites to choose from and frequently change from one day to the next. One

Where disturbance is low otters may take a nap in the open.

male used twenty-seven sites during three months of tracking, eighteen of which were above ground. These ranged from dense vegetation or substantial piles of sticks and branches to depressions in the bankside where the plants were only about 30 cm high. Most of those below ground were natural holes under the roots of trees or amongst rocks and boulders although one was an old rabbit burrow. More than ninety per cent of the sites were within fifty metres of the water and most of them within a few metres. Studies in Wales show that there trees such as ash and sycamore

Some dens are amongst rocks.

with large root systems are used by otters as the roots are undermined by the water, forming hidden ledges and caverns.

Otters living on the west coast of Scotland and the Scottish islands seem to have little difficulty in finding holes and caverns amongst the rocks and they too can be very adaptable. I have tracked otters into sand dunes where I suspect they lie up in enlarged rabbit burrows and they often burrow into the peat, sometimes creating what looks like a small badger sett with several entrances and well-worn paths between them. Coastal otters generally seem to have fewer dens than those radio-tracked along rivers in eastern Scotland but it is not clear whether this is due to differences in the sizes of home ranges or to the availability of suitable sites. Possibly both factors are important.

Perhaps the most important choice lies with the female in finding a good breeding den, and some people believe that the lack of suitable sites may prevent them from breeding in certain areas. The problem, of course, is in knowing what makes a good breeding site. Two otters radio-tracked in Scotland revealed dens with young cubs, one of which was forty metres from the river and the other at least a hundred metres from the nearest stream. These, together with three breeding dens found by Rosemary Harper in other parts of Scotland, had one feature in common which was that they were extremely unlikely to be flooded. It is also interesting that two of the dens Rosemary found were well away from the main river although both were near or beside small streams of half and one and a half metres in width. Clearly, close proximity to a large river is not essential for breeding dens and avoidance of flooding and the risk of disturbance might be more important in selection. The need for this is illustrated by an observation of James Williams's when he found evidence of a breeding den which had been flooded out after heavy rains. It was a rabbit burrow in a water meadow. That female otter had made a bad choice.

Geoff Liles compared five breeding sites he had discovered in Wales and two more he had been told about in England, trying to establish exactly what the otters needed. He found that there were some features in common. Most sites consisted of extensive areas (two hectares or more) of dense cover such as reedbeds, scrub or young conifer plantations. Sites were not necessarily on main rivers and some were beside lakes and ponds but they all seemed to have good sources of food nearby.

Dens where cubs are raised are not necessarily the same as those where they are born, and cub-rearing dens can be quite conspicuous in some places. Around the coast of Shetland, well-used cub-rearing dens may have substantial piles of spraint outside 10–15 cm high and 50 cm or so in diameter – hardly inconspicuous. There are also sufficient reports of otters raising their cubs in places which are moderately 'disturbed' to show that they don't have to choose places well away from people. The Shetland studies showed that busy ferry terminals (and even a major oil terminal) were acceptable to otters and, in the Second Survey of Scotland, Jim and Rosie Green reported four instances of cubs being born in and around the Glasgow conurbation.

One resource which is of great importance to otters living on the coast is fresh water. Not necessarily for drinking but for washing in. Otters which hunt in the sea need to be able to wash the salt out of their fur before they return to their dens – otherwise they can't do a thing with it the next day. More seriously, its waterproofing qualities are seriously impaired (see below).

One thing is certain, the continuing recovery of otter populations in the UK shows no signs of being slowed down or prevented by an absence of breeding opportunities.

So, where *do* otters live? Well, otters can be found living in freshwater, in estuaries and on the coast and, if it were not for the activities of man, they would probably be found in most freshwater, most estuaries and along much of the coast of Britain today. Man's influence is described in more detail later in the book. Here I will simply try to explain the natural influences on otter distribution.

There may be some places which could not support otters. Nevertheless, where otters are present, they will use every waterway that is available to them, including the tiniest streams.

I can remember visiting the Island of Coll, where the biggest stream is little more than two metres wide, and finding signs of otters throughout the island as well as on the coast. Tiny streams which had little food or shelter were used as routes through to the many lochs which are found inland. Tiny lochs, which might only have enough fish to support an otter for a short time, were also visited, though perhaps only occasionally so that the otters could feed on trout and eels there when it was too rough to feed at sea.

Similarly in south-west England, where I have looked at many culverts beneath roads to see whether otters might be forced to cross the carriageway, I find that signs of otters occur even where there is only a tiny trickle of water. There are some places where otters have been killed on roads because they followed up a watercourse which takes surface water from the road and only flows during heavy rains.

Some of the best freshwater habitat for otters is found along the large lowland streams of central and southern England. These are productive as well as being large and therefore have high densities of fish, particularly coarse fish. This is also the place where man has the greatest impact. I suspect that, at one time, the best habitat in England was the Norfolk

Broads. Not only were these extensive in area and highly productive but also very shallow, an important factor for otters when hunting.

Conversely, the lochs of the Scottish Highlands and the lakes of Cumbria have less to offer otters than those in the lowlands which are filled by water which has run off productive farmland rather than infertile hills, although they too are used by them.

Incidentally, although productive rivers are better than unproductive ones, large rivers are not always better than small. In northern Scotland on the rivers Dee and Don, otters spent more time hunting on the tributaries and small streams than the main river because the production of fish was greater there.

The seasons also play a part in determining the use otters make of an area. I remember visiting one small loch on Islay in the Inner Hebrides some years ago. It was about 600 m long and a kilometre from the sea. When we visited it in spring 1987 there were far more otter spraints than we had ever seen before and practically all of them contained the remains of frogs. Presumably the otters had been there earlier in the year at spawning time, harvesting the frogs as they came to the waterside for their annual mating spree. This is one reason why marshes, fens and other wetlands which contain little open water are also valuable otter habitat.

The extent to which otters use estuaries is hard to determine and no radio-tracking has been done in this habitat in the UK. They certainly do forage in estuaries but it is very difficult to find signs, perhaps because of the tidal range which washes them away. This habitat can be extremely productive, which is why wading birds are so abundant in it but it is not clear whether estuaries provide good foraging for otters. Certainly, the very deep estuaries found in parts of the south-west may have limited foraging because they shelve so steeply into water too deep for otters to reach the bottom where they prefer to forage.

Similar considerations apply to the coast. Productive areas are best but it is probably also important for coastal otters to have places where they can feed when seas are rough. Although there are some fish to be found where the sea bed is sandy, the best hunting is undoubtedly around rocky areas where seaweeds can gain a foothold and provide shelter and food for large numbers of fish. It is easier for otters to catch food in shallow water than deep, so gently shelving rocky shores are ideal.

The extent to which otters used to live around the coasts of England is unrecorded but I suspect that they were widespread in suitable areas. In Cornwall, people still speak of the times when otters were regularly seen around the coast and even today it is sometimes possible to find spraints where small streams flow out into the sea. Similarly, the mud flats and marshes of north Norfolk bordering the Wash were used by otters at least into the 1980s. However, it is Scotland that is best known for its coastal otters. Most of the west coast, the islands and part of the east coast are inhabited and it is to these areas that most people go when they want to see wild otters in Britain.

The very best habitat in Britain today may well be the east coast of the island of South Uist in the Outer Hebrides. Here there are a series of long finger-like sea lochs, some stretching two or three kilometres inland from the open sea. Sheltered, shallow and with alternative prey available in the small freshwater lochs on the land between them, these seem to have a very high density of otters. Even so, they are not easy to see, I spent three days there in the 1980s and did not spot a single one, though there were signs everywhere. Laura Bonesi made a similar pilgrimage during her studies of otters – with the same result! For me things improved with practice and, returning a few years later with a group of students, I had more luck and was able to impress them greatly at Loch Ainort where we had three sightings on our first morning of otter watching.

Gulls waiting for scraps.

Where otters sleep

The places where otters rest or sleep have several names, some of which are derived from hunting terminology. Thus 'holt' usually refers to some sort of tunnel and 'couches' are resting sites above ground. Hunters also talked about 'hovers' but I have never been entirely sure how these are defined. There is no single name that covers all the places that otters use other than 'resting sites' or 'dens', the latter usually implying an enclosed place.

One of the most comprehensive surveys of resting sites was made by Ian Coghill on the upper reaches of the Severn and its tributaries in Wales where he recorded 256. These were all known to otter hunters and some had been used for periods of twenty to forty years, while a few had been in use for a hundred years or more. All of the sites were close to water, ninety per cent within ten metres of the bank (many actually on the river bank) and the remainder within fifty metres of the waterside.

His largest category was tree holts, all but one of which consisted of tunnels into or under the root systems. The odd one out was a hollow trunk. Over ninety per cent of these had entrances leading directly into deep water and nearly three-quarters were under trees which leaned out over the water. Ash and sycamore were the favourite species having shallow spreading root systems, ideal roofs for otter dens.

Trees also provide shelter when they or their branches get swept down river in spates and large tangles accumulate to form stick piles. Coghill recorded thirty-four of these which were used by otters in his study area, some lasting for surprisingly long periods of time (forty years was the maximum). The otters seemed to prefer those that formed over water rather than on land, particularly if the water was deep.

Just over twenty per cent of the resting sites were of more solid material – rock or concrete – and many of these were formed artificially. Three were natural rock cavities but the remainder were

Spreading tree roots can provide good den sites.

either drains or heaps of rock, forming embankments or created as spoil from quarries.

Fifty-one of the sites came into the category 'lying rough'. These were above ground, usually in thick vegetation such as reed beds or osiers. They are probably even more common in low-lying places where the water table is near the surface than in the upper reaches of the Severn. When otters were common in the Norfolk Broads they would often use couches in the reedbeds, for breeding as well as for sleeping.

Coghill's final category was 'miscellaneous' and included rabbit burrows and badger setts together with one unique site – the back seat of a car that was ending its days as bank protection on a Welsh river.

When radio-tracking otters in Scotland, Jim and Rosemary Green found forty-eight resting sites, of which half were holts and half couches. Holts were usually tunnels in the river bank amongst roots and boulders while couches were mostly in dense vegetation such as sallow scrub or rhododendrons. A few of the couches were under piles of sticks and branches and one was in a depression amongst bankside vegetation which was only about 30 cm high. They realised that, for the most part, they would never have guessed that the couches were used by otters had it not been for the radio-transmitter betraying the animals' presence.

SIGNS OF OTTERS

One of the difficulties in studying shy and retiring animals like otters is just that – they are shy and retiring. In addition they are often nocturnal and usually scarce so it is hardly surprising that people studying them tend to spend more time looking for their signs than for the otters themselves. This is why the apparently arcane study of otter droppings, or spraints, is so important.

The significance of sprainting behaviour to otters is discussed in the chapter on communication but spraints are also of great interest to biologists, for two main reasons. The first is that they are a very good way of obtaining information about the otter's diet. Most food eaten by otters contains indigestible parts and these are eliminated in the faeces when they may be conveniently collected for study. The great advantage of using spraints in this way is that they are a constantly renewable source of material and this has enabled some people to collect a substantial amount

Young otter sprainting.

of information on the diet of otters. Second, the fact that you can find otter spraint on a river is a clear indication that otters have been there, something which is otherwise very difficult to confirm. Counting otter spraints does not tell you how many otters there are in an area but they are a useful guide to the otter's distribution at a regional and national level.

A recent addition to the technical armoury of ecologists is DNA fingerprinting, and this has been applied to otters as well as to humans and many other species of animal. The basic idea – pick up an otter's spraint, extract otter DNA from it (in cells from the gut lining) and then identify the animal from its genetic fingerprint – is attractive, and it does work. The problem is that it is still very expensive and not yet very reliable. Spraints need to be very fresh and even then you can't always extract good DNA from them. Nevertheless, it has great potential and preliminary studies suggest that there may be more otters around than we had thought.

Spraintology

The word 'spraint' was originally used by otter hunters in the British Isles but has now passed into common use, at least amongst those interested in otters. The word is believed to come from the French *épreindre*, 'to squeeze out'. The source of this information, *The Language of Field Sports* by C. E. Hare (who else?) includes about fifty words connected with otter hunting of which four are used for the otter's droppings ('spraint', 'wedging', 'coke' and, formerly, 'tredeles'). The origins of 'coke' I can understand as an otter spraint does have some resemblance to the derivative of coal but the origins of the others are less obvious. Thanks to the power of the World Wide Web, I discovered 'tredeles' in Volume 6 of the *Middle English Dictionary* by Robert E. Lewis. It is a synonym for 'tirdel', and comes from the Old English 'tyrdlu' (plural 'tyrdelu') which makes the link with modern English more obvious and suggests a possible pronunciation.

Zoologists often use the word 'scat' for faeces, particularly of carnivores, and 'scat' or 'spraint' can be used for otter droppings. It is most important to remember that only otters produce spraints if you want to maintain your credibility with otter enthusiasts. You might get away with using the words 'coke' and 'wedging' in conversation with otter hunters but I have never heard 'tredeles' used.

Otters have powerful digestions and only bones and fish scales pass right through the gut, together with fur, feathers and the skeletons of insects or crayfish, depending on the otter's diet. The presence of fish bones in a scat, particularly the spiky vertebrae, is usually a good indication that you have found an otter spraint, although mink is also a possibility (see *Spraints and scats* on the next page).

Another clue is the smell, which is not unpleasant and is added by special glands which discharge into the rectum. Scent seems to be important to otters for communication and spraints tend to be found in conspicuous places, sometimes in considerable numbers. The largest count I have heard of was of 250 spraints at one site. As spraint in the open tends to weather and disappear over a few weeks or months, such accumulations normally only occur in sheltered areas, under rocks and cliffs or in the entrances to dens.

Spraint sites seem, to humans at least, to be placed where other otters are likely to encounter them. Conspicuous features of the river bank such as large rocks, the bases of bridges or large trees are often used while, on the coast, concentrations of spraints are found near dens, rolling places and freshwater pools. Where the soil is infertile, for example on the west coast of Scotland, otter spraints can often be located because the grass is particularly lush and green where it has been regularly fertilised.

Sometimes otters will scrape up sand, mud or even grass to form a small heap, usually called a 'sign heap', on which they deposit their spraint.

Where good spraint are scarce, otters may make sign heaps.

Spraints and scats

Otter spraints are not too difficult to find when you know where to look (assuming otters are present) but they can easily be confused at first with such things as twigs, leaves, moss and bird droppings. A close inspection will enable you to discard some of these fairly readily. Most bird droppings consist of very fine material which has been ground down in the gizzard (part of the stomach forming a muscular sac with grit in it for grinding food) and, although the appearance may be somewhat gritty, the particles are usually very fine. There is often some white material (uric acid) in bird droppings though not always. A good indication that you have either an otter spraint or a mink scat is the presence of fish bones which are usually quite small (1–3 mm across) and are distinctly spiky, or scales which are thin and translucent.

A 'textbook' otter spraint is 6–8 cm long and about 1 cm in diameter, cylindrical and full of tiny spiky fish bones or scales. The colour is very variable from black or dark greenish-brown to very pale grey, depending partly on age. A well-weathered spraint can look like the result of leaving a cigar on an ashtray to burn away undisturbed.

Needless to say, textbook descriptions do not cover all eventualities and spraints can be much smaller than this as otters use them for communication (see later) and produce small spraints for marking purposes. Occasionally you will encounter no more than a tarry splodge, perhaps with a few fish bones in it. Fortunately the only likely source of confusion with otter spraint is mink scats and these are often quite distinctive.

One of the best characteristics, at least in fresh specimens, is smell, since both species add a unique scent to their faeces from glands discharging into the rectum. Mink scats smell quite unpleasant when fresh although the odour fades over a few days. Otter spraints, on the other hand, have an inoffensive smell which is very characteristic. Usually described as musky or musty, sometimes as fishy or spicy, it was once likened to the scent of laurel. C. E. Hare, author of *The Language of Field Sports*, says, 'It is agreeably scented, like snuff.'

My own view is that it is best described as 'ottery' and the only way to learn it is to get someone else to show you a spraint so that you can make up your own mind. One friend likens it to the scent of jasmine tea – which may explain why I am not a tea drinker.

There are also differences in appearance. Mink scats are smaller and thinner than the 'typical' otter spraints, perhaps 5–7 cm in length and about 7 mm in diameter. Usually tapering and sometimes twisted at the ends, they tend to be much more compact than spraints which are rather loosely formed.

The contents of scats are not necessarily a good guide, because mink eat a similar range of prey to otters although they take a much higher proportion of birds and mammals. However, fresh spraints/scats containing fish are probably the easiest to distinguish and, once you have learned to separate these, it is possible to graduate onto older specimens and those containing fur or feathers. Even so, there will always be some which cannot be assigned to one species or the other.

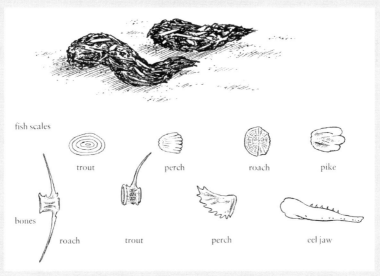

Typical otter spraint (above) and typical contents (below).

At one time it was thought that sign heaps might have a special significance but I have found them mainly on smooth stretches of sand or mud. Where there was nothing obvious to spraint on, the otter appeared to have constructed a spraint site for itself. One particularly industrious otter scraped up a total of forty-eight sign heaps around the shore of a small pool in south Devon during January, 1976. Most of these had a small spraint on top. Heaps of shingle were often found around the nearby lake which, in some areas, had a rather barren shore line with few trees or rocks to provide suitable spraint sites.

Otters are capable of quite remarkable feats of agility in using some spraint sites. More than once I have found spraint on horizontal branches only 15 cm or so in diameter – quite a balancing act. Another spraint site that I have seen was three metres up in the branches of an old oak tree leaning over the river Wye. If Welsh otters are good climbers, Scottish otters seem to have good heads for heights; the most intriguing spraint site I have found was beside a freshwater pool at the top of a fifty metre cliff in the Hebrides. The spraints were deposited only centimetres from a sheer drop to the sea below. It was certainly a loo with a view.

In contrast, people have sometimes seen otters sprainting in water and it has been suggested that this may be a special strategy adopted by females when they have young cubs. By not sprainting on land they may reduce the risks of predators finding and eating the cubs. Otter hunters certainly believed that females with cubs produced no scent.

Occasionally you will find a substance which smells like spraint but consists of a jelly-like material with no bones or scales in it. Various names have been used for this, 'tarry-spraints' and 'anal jelly' are the most frequent and the latter is probably the best as it is suggestive of the origin – the otter's anal glands. It seems to be blobs of secretion from these glands though the significance is obscure. It may be no more complex than the otter using it to deposit its scent when it has 'run out' of faeces. It does seem to be a better source of otter DNA than spraint, though, perhaps because it has not been involved in the digestive process.

Tracks and other signs

One can of course look for other signs of the presence of otters and the best alternative to spraints is footprints. Otters, like all mustelids, have five toes, whereas cats and dogs have only four. This means that if you have a clear print you only have to distinguish it from the tracks of mink and polecat, which are smaller, and badger, which are larger, to be sure that you are looking at an otter's footprint. Very occasionally, if you are lucky, you may find a print in soft mud in which the webs can be seen.

Needless to say, life is not always that kind. Very often you will find a nice patch of mud which has a confused mass of footprints, pitted by rain drops, trodden by people and dogs and with one or two faint prints at the edge which you hope might just be otter. Also it is surprising how often you find 'four-toed' otters because the smallest toe does not make a mark, especially in firm mud or in sand. Even so, it may still be possible to recognise the prints perhaps by searching for one really good one. With experience you can distinguish a four-toed otter from a dog or fox print because the dog and fox both have very symmetrical prints whereas those of the otter are lopsided.

Although the best places to find footprints are usually at the waterside, on patches of mud or sand, otters also travel across land from time to time and sometimes make quite distinct trails. These are most easily seen in coastal areas where you find well-worn paths connecting up dens,

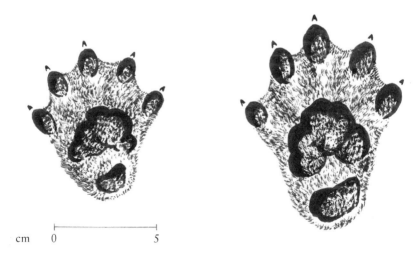

cm   0   5

The underside of an otter's right front foot (left) and (right) hind foot.

freshwater pools and rolling places or around lakes where otters may take short cuts across peninsulas or have paths running to dens near the water. You can also find them on rivers, particularly those that meander a great deal. Otters will sometimes miss out a large loop in the river and run across the land to pick it up again. These trails are usually marked at intervals by spraints and, where there is a steep drop into the river, you may find a 'slide'.

Sliding into the water.

30

Slides used to be thought of as otter playing places, and some are occasionally used as such, but those that I have seen have simply been where otters clamber up a steep bank out of the water or slip back in again. They remind me very much of the badger 'up-and-overs' we see on hedge banks in Devon. These are badger crossing places and get very worn by the regular passage of heavy badger feet but they are not used primarily for play.

The other signs of otters you may find are their dens (holts) and the remains of their meals. It can be quite difficult to distinguish between some otter dens and simple holes in the bank and the best way of confirming that an otter uses such a hole is to find footprints or spraints beside it. What you should not do is try to find out whether there is an otter inside by peering in, poking with a stick or shining a torch. These could be considered disturbance to an otter in its den which is an offence.

It is rather similar with prey remains. Distinguishing between a fish that has been partially eaten by an otter and one that a mink has eaten is tricky. Again the presence or footprints or spraints nearby is the best way to be sure. It is a little easier with coastal dens, particularly those under rocks or amongst boulders. They usually have a well-worn path leading to them and spraint in or around the entrance.

Incidentally, country people, especially water bailiffs, tell stories about otters which would catch a whole salmon, take 'one bite out of the shoulder' and leave it on the bank, where of course, it can be collected by the bailiff and safely 'disposed of'. I am quite sure that this happened occasionally but perhaps not as often as is sometimes suggested and the bite out of the shoulder was probably a good deal more than that. One description suggested that the otter had eaten 'more than a pound of flesh' – a very good meal for an otter but leaving plenty for the bailiff to consume since otters are known to have occasionally caught salmon up to nine kilos in weight!

WHERE CAN I SEE OTTERS?

A frequent question and usually, I suspect, asked in the hope that I can recommend somewhere close to hand where you can easily pop down to the waterside for a pleasant evening's otter watching. It is not that easy, at least, not in southern Britain where the question is usually asked.

In theory at least, you ought to be able to see otters wherever they can be found and, armed with the distribution map on page 131, you could head for the river bank and settle down to wait. I reckon that in most areas where otters are doing reasonably well, a fortnight of waiting should normally be enough. In most places otters ought to pass you two or three times during that time. Not that you will see much, unless you are very lucky, or have special equipment for night viewing; even then an otter could slip past without being noticed. Over a period of two years when I spent many nights otter watching on a lake where they passed the same spot on most nights I never had more than a brief glimpse: sometimes a v-shaped wake as the otter swam under the bridge; once or twice a ghostly humped back on the far bank as it went to its spraint site; on one very bright night I had a really clear view as one swam towards me, dived as it came close to the bridge I was sitting beside, and then swam underwater past me, just visible through my binoculars. A few people

The v-shaped wake

have become successful otter watchers in southern parts of Britain but it needs a tremendous amount of persistence in the face of a very high proportion of unsuccessful nights. An ability to do without sleep is a great asset not to mention an understanding employer, or at least an occupation you can carry out on autopilot.

On the whole, in southern Britain I have always recommended the enthusiastic otter spotter to take up badger watching; it's much more productive. Badgers are a great deal more common than otters and are found more or less throughout Britain. They are reasonably predictable, usually coming out of the same hole each night at about the same time, and they have nice stripy faces to help you see them in the half dark – much simpler and just as exciting.

Alternatively, of course, you could move to Scotland, preferably the west coast or one of the islands. Not only are otters more abundant in good coastal habitats than in less productive freshwater ones but they are also much more likely to come out during the day.

At one time, the best technique for seeing otters in Scotland seemed to be to make sure I was not with you when you were looking for them. Many times people saw them just before or just after I had visited a place and there are countless spots where I have been assured, 'You are certain to see otters there', but have failed to do so. More practically, the best thing to do is to walk quietly and keep scanning the water surface and shore line. Binoculars are usually essential, not least for eliminating the numerous otter-like things you will see, seals and fronds of kelp in particular. (I once spent ten minutes carefully scrutinising a hooded crow that was pretending to be an otter.) Sooner or later, though, you will be lucky and may have a very rewarding experience. Once, for example, after we had been watching one otter feeding on a Scottish sea loch for about half an hour, it disappeared. After ten minutes we got up to continue our walk only to find two more padding down the beach towards us. Whether these were dim, over-confident or just short-sighted I don't know, but they ambled down to the water's edge about fifty metres away from three humans and two dogs and proceeded to fish in full view for about forty-five minutes.

Apart from keeping quiet and being watchful, I don't believe there are any other rules for otter watching in coastal areas. It is obviously well worth listening to locals who will often know of places where they may be seen but I suspect you are just as likely, perhaps even more likely, to find them elsewhere, off the beaten track where people do not go very often. My most successful otter spotting was in Shetland when helping with a survey there, where I had ten sightings in a week.

More recently I have had two 'accidental' sightings of otters in England. The first was at night when, watching Daubenton's bats foraging low over the water, I was shocked to see two bright red eyes glowing in the torchlight as an otter swam towards me, briefly left the water, and then dived back in and swam out of sight under the bridge. The other was in broad daylight when I was actually doing an otter survey and saw what looked like a log steadily moving upstream pushing a distinct ripple before it. With over thirty years of doing otter surveys in England that is an average of once every fifteen years.

For inland waters I have one helpful tip: take up fishing. I think I have had more reports of otter sightings from people who go night fishing for sea-trout than any other single activity. I have also heard of one unfortunate otter which was disturbed from his daytime slumber by the activities of biologists studying fish in the river Otter in east Devon. The otter dived into the stream to escape, not realising that they were using electric fishing equipment. It must have been a stunning experience; I understand it broke the world record for diving into a river and straight back out again.

Finally, of course, there are otters in a number of zoos although these are not usually the Eurasian species (Asian short-clawed are most common). Check before you go to a wildlife park or zoo advertising otters if you want to be sure of seeing European ones. Places which do have them include the Chestnut Centre Otter, Owl and Wildlife Park, Chapel-en-le-Frith, Derbyshire, the New Forest Wildlife Park, Marchwood, Hampshire and the Buckfast Butterflies & Dartmoor Otter Sanctuary, Buckfastleigh, Devon. At each of these you can compare them with other species.

SIZE, SHAPE AND APPEARANCE

With its distinctive hump-backed gait, short legs, long neck, body and tail, the otter is quite easy to recognise when seen in the open in broad daylight. However, it is surprising how often otters are confused with other animals, particularly mink. Very often this is due to lack of knowledge and experience. A colleague who travelled with great excitement to a Midland river where otters had confidently, but surprisingly, been identified in the 1970s was somewhat disillusioned when she was proudly shown water voles, some thirty times smaller than a female otter! However, it must be said that sightings are frequently not under ideal conditions and I have been fooled when what I thought was an otter swimming across a pool turned out to be a mink. Most embarrassing, since it was the mink I was radio-tracking at the time.

cat

otter

mink

Mink, otter and a fairly large cat.

Another source of confusion, though normally only on the coast, is seals. These are much larger than otters and, when seen close to, their relatively larger eyes and narrower muzzles are obvious. Seals tend to rest vertically in the water with only their noses or heads showing whereas otters more often lie horizontally with their back and sometimes their tail at the surface. It is, of course, easy to be confused, particularly if the animal is not close and the sea is a little choppy. You might think that you would be safe on a river, but beware: seals do venture quite long distances inland and have reached as far

as St Ives on the river Ouse for example, over 60 km from the Wash as the crow flies and rather more as the seal swims.

The following comparisons should help in recognising an otter and distinguishing it from the animal it is most likely to be confused with, the mink.

Comparison of mink and otter

	MINK	OTTER
Size	Smaller than the average cat.	Larger than the largest cat.
Colour	Dark brown, almost black.	Mid brown when dry but may appear much darker when wet. After shaking, the wet coat may have a spiky appearance.
Patterns	Underside same colour as back but distinct white spots may be visible under chin (may also be on chest and abdomen).	Underside usually paler than back. May have white or cream patch under chin but not distinct.
Shape	Pointed face, thinner than a dachshund.	Flattened wedge-shaped head with broad whiskery muzzle. More stretched corgi than dachshund in size.
Tail	Bushy and cylindrical like a cat's tail. Half the length of the body.	Stout at the base, tapering to a point. About 40% of body length.
Behaviour	Curious and apparently unafraid of humans. Often hunts by diving into water from bank, rock or log. Regularly seen in daylight.	Somewhat shy and retiring, tends to avoid humans. Hunts by diving repeatedly in same area from surface of the water. Not often seen in daylight except in coastal areas.

LIVING IN WATER

Living, or even just hunting, in water presents many problems which land animals do not have to face. In particular, water is cold, dense and lacks oxygen. There are ways to overcome all these difficulties and, if you look closely at whales, dolphins and seals, you will soon recognise many of them. Thus they all have a torpedo-shaped body and smooth skin so that they can slip easily through the water (no sharp projections like shoulders to create drag). Flipper-like feet provide good propulsion in water and plenty of blubber helps to smooth the edges and keep the warmth in. The trick that the otter has had to accomplish is how to be sufficiently good at living in water to be able to catch fish in their natural element, while being reasonably proficient at moving on land where it still spends much of its time.

Otters are well adapted to life in water ...

... but swimming must be practised.

It is no coincidence then that the long sinuous body of a typical mustelid seems to be well adapted for an aquatic life. Swimming for their supper has evolved more than once in the family (otters and two species of mink) and both whales and seals had long-bodied, otter-like ancestors. Since otters spend a lot of time out of water, it is not surprising that the body shape of the semi-aquatic otter is very similar to its terrestrial cousins such as polecat and pine marten. Apart perhaps from the stout tail and slightly over-sized feet, one would be hard put to find any characteristic of the otter's skeleton or skull which pointed to its aquatic way of life. It is only when you begin to look at the soft parts that you find the subtle but important differences between otters and their close relatives which are due to their aquatic habits.

Perhaps the most obvious feature is the webbing on an otter's feet. This extends for much of the length of each digit although not to the very end. It is not unique – dogs have distinct, though less extensive, webs between their toes but, not surprisingly, the otter has developed them much further. The paws are also a little larger than one might expect, probably to provide a bit more push when swimming. Incidentally, this is carried to extremes in the two largest species, giant otters and sea otters, which look as if they are wearing clown's boots on their hind feet.

The otter's tail is stout at the base and tapers towards the tip where it is noticeably flattened. Although it was sometimes called the rudder by otter hunters, it is not flattened from side to side but from top to bottom because it forms part of the propulsion unit. When swimming fast underwater, the hind end of the body moves up and down as the hind feet kick together.

Keeping warm and dry is important to otters and, like many other mammals, their fur consists of two types of hair: stout guard hairs which may be up to 2 cm long and form a waterproof outer covering, plus a denser, finer layer of underfur which constitutes the otter's thermal underwear. Because they have to spend so much time in water, otters have developed an extremely thick coat (which is why their skins used to be prized in the fur trade). A Canadian scientist once counted the hairs on patches of otter skin and concluded that there were about 60,000 per square centimetre (not far short of 400,000 per square inch). Sea otters, which spend their whole lives in the sea, have fur which is twice as dense.

The fur must be kept in good condition and grooming is a very important part of otter life. It has been shown that sea water reduces the waterproofing qualities of otter fur and this is why freshwater pools are so important to otters living on the coast. When they have finished swimming they wash the salt off in the pools and then squirm on the ground nearby to rub themselves dry against the vegetation. If they are unable to wash in fresh water, salt crystals begin to form in the fur and the guard hairs clump together. The fur becomes lifeless and loses its normal fluffy appearance as well as its insulating properties in the water.

Another aid to keeping warm is to have a high metabolic rate. All mammals are able to adjust their metabolism to circumstances and have various ways of maintaining their body at a constant temperature. Small mammals, like shrews, have a relatively large surface area and lose heat quickly so they have a high metabolic rate, while large ones, like elephants, can afford to tick over more slowly.

Otters suffer from two disadvantages when it comes to heat retention. The first is their body shape; long thin animals have a larger surface area than animals which are the same size but more compact. In fact, the most

efficient shape to be if you want to minimise heat loss is a sphere. This problem faces most of the weasel family, and a high metabolic rate is normal in the family. The second problem is that they forage in water, which leads to even greater heat loss. Not surprising, then, that if you compare otters with similarly sized animals that do not hunt in water you will find that their metabolism is about twenty per cent higher to compensate for the fact that they lose heat more rapidly in water than in air. Despite this they can still get chilled if they stay in water too long, particularly if they are hunting in deeper water where the air is squeezed out of their fur more quickly, reducing its effectiveness in insulation. Coastal otters will only fish for fifteen minutes or so before coming ashore to groom, rest and warm up.

This creates a bit of a conundrum for otters and probably has a significant impact on where they can live. Higher metabolic rates have to be fuelled by a higher food intake. Catching more food means spending more time in the water which leads to higher energy consumption. Where the water is very cold, otters may only be able to survive if food is particularly abundant and easy to catch.

Grooming – the final touches.

OTTER SENSES

Semi-aquatic animals like otters have to face entirely different sensory problems in the two media in which they live. The properties of air and water are so different that senses which work well in one may be much less effective in another. A simple example is the sense of smell. Noses work very well in air. Each breath sucks past the sensory organs a large sample of air in which various compounds, present in minute quantities, can be detected, analysed and often identified. Of course, the air is on its way down to the lungs where it has an important role to play in respiration, so any attempt to sample water using the same process would have catastrophic consequences. Not that the olfactory (smell detecting) organs would mind – air and water are both good carriers of scent – but, because the mammalian nose is used for breathing as well as smelling, sniffing under water is not a good idea.

There has been a suggestion that otters might be able to use the sensitive skin around their nostrils to 'taste' underwater but there is no firm evidence for this. Nevertheless, scent does have an important part to play in their lives, far greater than for humans. This should not be too surprising since otters spend more of their time out of the water than in it and much activity takes place on land. Like other carnivores, they undoubtedly use scent for hunting on land, even if they cannot in water. Scent also has an important role in communication and probably in detecting danger as well. No-one has tested the sensitivity of the otter nose but it seems likely that it is similar to that of other carnivores like dogs and is much better than ours.

Otters' eyes are not very large and, compared to humans, they seem to be quite short-sighted on land but their vision is certainly adequate at short distances. When light passes from one medium to another (from air to water or from either to glass) the rays are bent. You can see this if you hold a pencil or stick half in water; it appears to bend at the junction. This property (refraction) is of enormous benefit to mankind because it allows us to manufacture lenses. Without refraction there would be no microscopes, no binoculars, no cameras – come to that no eyes either, at least not like the ones we have now. However, because the degree of bending varies depending on which two media light is passing between,

Small eyes and ears but very large whiskers.

eyes which are adapted to see in air have major problems in focussing in water. Humans overcome this problem by putting a layer of air (and glass) between the surface of the eye and the water but otters have overcome the same problem without resorting to goggles. In clear water and bright light otters can focus and resolve fine detail as well as in air because they can modify the shape of the lens to make it more spherical. So on a bright sunny day in a clear moorland stream otters are able to hunt by sight. Unfortunately, otters often have to hunt in murky water and on dark nights, yet they still manage to catch fish. How do they do it?

A simple but elegant series of experiments by Jim Green showed how. He timed two captive otters catching fish in a clear pool and then again in the same pool after he had tipped in a quantity of powdered charcoal. This made the water so dark that a shiny metal object could only be seen if it was less than 10 cm from the surface. Both otters took four times longer to catch fish in the dark than in clear water. One of the otters was then given a trim. The long whiskers (vibrissae) growing around his muzzle were all cut back (they grew again afterwards). In clear water he was just as successful at catching fish as before but this time, in the darkened water, he took twenty times as long. So it seems that the vibrissae are used to detect the presence of fish when otters are unable to use their eyes. Rather than feel the fish direct the whiskers probably detect the regular vibrations caused by the beat of the fish's tail as it swims away from the otter. Interestingly, studies of the otter's brain have shown that the area which deals with signals coming in from the facial area of river otters and giant otters is larger than normal. Sea otters and clawless otters by contrast have an enlarged area dealing with information coming from their sensitive forepaws. Some otters use their paws for feeling for food, with clawless otters and sea otters being particularly adept at this. Karl Kenyon once set a sea otter the task of finding four mussels in a bucket containing two hundred crabs and several pebbles. The otter only took a few seconds to remove the mussels from the muddy water, leaving the other contents in the bucket. It is quite likely that Eurasian otters use touch when finding slow-moving or immobile prey.

Otter's external ears are tiny but this is probably due more to streamlining than to the fact that they are unimportant. Indeed, otters seem to have quite sensitive hearing, much better than ours, and Philip Wayre has suggested that they can respond to sounds inaudible to humans. Once again this is fine on land but different in the water. Water transmits sound very well, far better than air, but this turns out to be a disadvantage in some ways. The problem is that, although you can hear sounds well underwater, it is almost impossible to determine which way they are coming from unless you have special modifications to the parts of the ear within the head. Otters do not have these adaptations (although dolphins do) so it seems unlikely that they use sound for locating prey under water. Incidentally, you may think that fish do not make much noise so sound would not be any good for finding them. This may well be the case but you should remember that, like bats, some whales, dolphins and possibly some seals use echo-location to find their prey.

So, to summarise: in air, sound, scent and sight are the most important senses, in that order; below the surface of the water, sight and feel are used.

LOCOMOTION

Otters are not the most graceful of creatures on land. They don't quite waddle but their hump-backed gait is not the most elegant means of locomotion. Nor are they particularly fast movers, but that is hardly surprising given their short legs and flat-footed stance. Walking is the preferred means of getting about but, if pressed, an otter will break into a run or a bounding gallop. It has been claimed that the American river otter can run as fast as a man but this probably depends on the circumstances. On the flat a man would undoubtedly be able to outpace an otter but Jim Conroy found that it was not so easy along the river bank, especially if you are carrying a typical field biologist's equipment such as radio-receiver, antenna, notebooks, night viewer and so on. I know of no-one who has timed a Eurasian otter on land but a spotted-necked otter was timed at 1.4 metres per second (3.1 mph) when running and 2 metres per second (4.5 mph) when galloping, not much more than a vigorous walk for a human.

When otters make substantial journeys, they usually do so in the water, travelling at the surface, although occasional short cuts may be made across land, at large meanders for example, when visiting isolated lakes or crossing watersheds. Considerable distances can be covered in this way. Don Jefferies once followed an otter swimming down a Suffolk river for nearly eight hours during which it covered 11 km, an average speed of about 0.4 m/sec (just under 1 mph).

In water, of course, they are much more at home. Swimming at the surface is accomplished by a sort of dog-paddle using all four legs. Interestingly there seems to be no fixed pattern to this. Rather than using the typical walking pattern of most mammals, otters adopt a more casual approach sometimes kicking all four legs alternately, sometimes with two from the same side or two from the same end. They may even thrust with all four together. The same applies underwater when swimming slowly but, if the otter needs to accelerate, it kicks with the hind legs together. As it does so the back undulates up and down so that the hind end of the body, including the tail, functions as a unit providing a powerful thrust. While swimming in a straight line it tucks its forepaws into its chest bringing them into action for steering. Otters are not averse to getting a

Coming up ...

Going down ...

The Loch Ness monster?

bit of extra push off the bottom, either with the front legs in steering or with the back to gain speed. Film of otters swimming often shows them using boulders, submerged logs or the bottom in this way and sometimes they can give the game away by pushing off the side of an artificial pool which has been made to look like natural habitat.

Although otters are clearly much more graceful in water than on land they do not move as quickly. The spotted-necked otter mentioned above achieved speeds of 1.1 metres per second (2.5 mph) in water and it has been estimated that the Eurasian otter swims at about that speed underwater.

Of course, all this vigorous exercise uses up oxygen and the size of the otter has a major influence on the length of time it can stay submerged. Large animals can hold their breath for very much longer than small ones so you might expect that otters would normally dive for quite short times compared to humans. Nevertheless people are often surprised to find that otter dives are usually less than thirty seconds and that dives in excess of forty-five seconds are very rare. In extremis otters can probably survive for about three minutes before drowning.

Otters normally dive from the surface of the water and probably only launch themselves from the bank when frightened. The surface dive is quite distinctive with the back forming a graceful arch and the hind legs and tail following it down into the water. This rolling dive is not unlike that used by large whales and seems to help drive the animal down into the water, an important benefit since otters usually hunt near the bottom. When they are swimming rapidly near the surface they use a series of shallow dives, breaking the surface every ten metres or so.

COMMUNICATION

Eurasian otters are not particularly sociable animals and, if you see a small group, the chances are that it is a family, consisting of the female with her young, or the young on their own. Two otters together may sometimes be a breeding pair but since courtship lasts only a few days before the sexes separate this is less likely. The more sociable otters, such as Asian small-clawed and giant otters, have quite a repertoire of calls and chatter noisily to one another but the lonely Eurasian otter is not a particularly vocal animal. Philip Wayre had more opportunity to get to know their language than most as he bred otters many times and hand-reared several. He recognised three main types of call.

The first is the famous otter whistle, actually a high-pitched squeak which is mainly used for keeping contact. Philip Wayre translated it as 'I'm here. Where are you?' It carries quite a way and is the sound most people associate with otters. (Incidentally, hearing a whistle on the river bank at night does not necessarily mean an otter. I am afraid there are a whole range of animals along the waterside whistling and squeaking away

pretending to be otters so it is not a reliable clue.) A quieter call, the 'hah' sound, is used by females to warn cubs of danger but it may also be used at times of unease or when an animal is startled or frightened. It sounds like a sharp exhalation of breath.

Then there are a number of more complex noises variously described as chittering, chuckling, whickering and twittering. The exact nature depends on the circumstances. High-pitched calls indicate annoyance or threat while a quieter, lower tone is used in greeting. Cubs make twittering noises when they are very young, perhaps to indicate to the female that they are hungry. Otters are noisiest of all when mating but there is no agreement on how to describe the sounds that are used: 'chirruping', 'purring', 'yarring' come from one report and 'harsh purring, staccato grunts and squeaks' from another. No doubt the otters understand what it all means.

It is equally difficult for humans to understand the exact meanings in another important form of communication between otters – scent, although some attempts have been made to find out at least what sort of information might be passed on. Most attention has been paid to the anal glands which discharge a rich cocktail of chemicals into the rectum and thereby taint the otter's faeces. This is what gives spraint its distinctive smell and, while people sometimes describe it as being fishy, this has nothing to do with the diet; spraints containing only mammal remains smell exactly the same.

Chemical analysis of the contents shows that although all spraints smell similar (to humans) there are differences between the scent of one otter and another. However, the scent 'profile' of one otter remains constant over periods of several weeks. One compound seems to be present in quite large quantities and this may be the one which humans notice and which gives the characteristic 'ottery' odour to spraints. Others are much more variable in quantity and might be used to distinguish individuality. As far as we know there is no indication of the sex of the animal in its scent but it seems quite likely that otters can tell how recently the spraint was deposited because the various constituents evaporate at different rates. Just as with *Chanel No. 5*, fresh scent is quite different from stale. Males seem to travel round their ranges refreshing the scent marks every few days. When they do not it seems to take less than a week for other otters to realise that this is no longer happening (see below).

Experiments with captive otters show that they are able to recognise the scents of individuals although we still do not know exactly how this information might be used in the wild. Nevertheless it is obvious that scent communication plays a very important part in otters' lives because of the amount of time they invest in it. Not only do otters take the trouble to leave their spraints where other otters are likely to find them but they also spend quite a lot of time investigating those they find at each spraint site before turning round and depositing another addition to the bulletin-board.

In a very careful study of the distribution of spraint sites on the west coast of Scotland, Beverly Trowbridge found that spraints were clumped around potential dens, resting sites and freshwater pools. These 'spraint stations' were spread along the coast so that otters coming ashore from the sea were likely to come across one very quickly. Where there were trails heading inland, often beside small streams, spraints were distributed at random but with a density of twenty per kilometre. Any otter following

Typical spraint site

51

a trail would be likely to encounter a spraint very soon.

So, what is the scent for? Well the answer is that we aren't really sure. It was once said that it was used as a territory marker and certainly in areas where otters are strongly territorial there is evidence that it has an important role to play. The best evidence comes from Sweden where Sam Erlinge observed that when a male died its territory was taken over within a week by a male from a neighbouring, less desirable territory. This was despite the fact that up to that time it had never been known to venture beyond a narrow zone of overlap between the territories and may reflect the time it takes for the scent to fade. Even so, although neighbours may not intrude too far, it is quite clear that itinerant otters do enter the territories of residents, so scent is not simply a warning to keep out or, if it is, it is not always effective. One theory suggests that it may enable trespassers to know when they have met the territory owner. If they encounter an otter which smells the same as most of the spraints in the area, it must be the resident. Since only big strong otters are likely to be territory holders it is probably a good idea to avoid confrontation and keep out the way. The intruder gains by avoiding a fight with a potentially superior rival, and the resident by demonstrating its superiority in an indirect manner rather than a costly and risky show of force.

Studies by Hans Kruuk of the sprainting habits of otters on the coast of Shetland suggested that here they were marking areas where they had been fishing. In an area where females often share territories with their offspring or sisters this means that close relatives will know that the local fish will have been eaten, or at least disturbed, already.

This argument may not apply in other areas. For example, it is hard to reconcile with an observation made by Jim and Rosemary Green on a river. They were able to mark the spraints of their female otters and showed that only a small proportion of the spraints in their home ranges were produced by the females themselves. They marked at a much lower rate than the adult male in a nearby area suggesting a difference in marking behaviour between the sexes. There is obviously still a lot to learn about the significance of scent marking in otters.

Many mammals have more than one type of scent gland, indeed some have a positive armoury. However, apart from the anal glands, the only other source of scent that has been seriously considered in otters is urine. Male otters do not seem to use urine to scent mark in the way that domestic dogs do but it is possible that there are compounds in the urine of female otters in breeding condition that would have the same effect as that of female dogs in season – a powerful attractant to the opposite sex! The chances of stumbling across a female in oestrous would be greatly enhanced if she were able to leave an odorous message around her range signalling her availability.

In order to investigate this Beverly Trowbridge managed to collect regular samples of the urine of a captive female otter by concealing a suitable receptacle under a layer of sand where the otter normally urinated. However, chemical analyses of the urine, although revealing changes in concentrations of hormones over time, did not show any clear evidence that they could be linked with the oestrous cycle.

FINDING AND CATCHING PREY

Like all good carnivores, otters adapt their hunting behaviour to circumstances and the techniques for catching fish, frogs, rabbits and ducks are naturally very different. Needless to say, most observations of otter hunting behaviour are limited to the time spent on the surface between dives for fish and there are very few reports of what happens under water or when otters hunt on land. Once again we have to piece together information from captive animals with snippets of information from the wild.

It seems that otters hunting fish probably use sight to find them where the water is reasonably clear but in dark or turbid water they either have to rely on their whiskers detecting the beat of a fish's tail or find them by feel. In still water, fish which do not move might be safe but the disturbance

Small prey are consumed in the water.

caused by the otter's searching may well be enough to put a fish to flight and thereby let the otter know it is there. In running water fish would need to swim just to keep still but whether otters would be able to distinguish the beat of a fishy tail from the turbulence of water tumbling over rocks we do not know. The river would no doubt produce greater vibrations but perhaps the regularity of the tail-beat would help the otter. Otters seem to forage under stones and amongst weed in order to try and flush out their prey. In Shetland they hunt mainly on the bottom and spend more time feeding in areas where the beds of seaweed are patchy and have longer 'edges' than in solid masses of kelp.

Species of otters that eat a lot of slow-moving invertebrate prey such as sea otters, short-clawed and clawless otters, use their sensitive forepaws for searching, feeling into nooks and crannies as well as under stones. It is possible that Eurasian otters do this do for some prey items too, particularly for crayfish or for species of fish that tend to sit tight on the bottom.

Captive otters in clear pools seem to hunt fish from below, perhaps because it is harder for the fish to detect them that way or it may be easier for the otter to see the fish. No-one knows how many chases end in failure in the wild but Philip Wayre found that if the fish managed to get more than two or three metres ahead it was safe, at least for the time being. In fact it is quite remarkable that otters can catch some species of fish at all because they have tremendous acceleration. A twenty-five centimetre trout can travel about two metres in the first second of flight but it quickly tires and, over a period of ten seconds, its average speed would come much closer to that of the otter. Indeed the otter's main strategy with fast swimming fish is probably to try and tire them out by chasing them persistently. In fairly shallow water this is not too difficult and hunting otters seem to be able to snatch a quick gulp of air at the surface without pausing in their pursuit. In deeper water, however, the otter has to return to the surface every so often to breathe and this gives its quarry ample time to escape or hide. This is probably why otters hunting in the sea concentrate mainly on slower-swimming bottom-dwelling fish.

In fact the need to breath must severely restrict the depth of water in which otters can fish, at least for bottom living species. In water ten metres deep an otter might need to spend as much as twenty seconds in travelling from the surface to the bottom and back again which does not leave much time for hunting. This probably explains why in Shetland Hans Kruuk found that nearly two-thirds of dives were in water less than three metres deep even though this made up less than a quarter of the area easily available to them, and otters were sometimes seen to hunt in water up to fourteen metres deep. The tidal range in Shetland is not very great but even so the otters hunted less at high tide than at other times. Elsewhere the state of the tide could be even more important in determining when otters feed.

Once the otter gets close enough it will grab the fish in its jaws, although sometimes the front paws are used as well. Small fish are eaten at the surface so that the otter can quickly resume hunting but larger specimens are carried to the shore and consumed at the waterside. Captive otters will sometimes 'play' with their food, especially eels which are not easily killed, but whether this happens much in the wild is unclear. It seems more likely that it would occur with young otters, learning to hunt,

Large prey may be eaten on land.

56

rather than adults.

Not every dive is successful, of course. Many end with the otter returning to the surface empty-handed or, at least, empty-mouthed. Around the coast, otters come up with prey on a quarter to a third of their dives but otters hunting on a freshwater loch two or three metres deep only caught prey on one out of fourteen dives. However, the freshwater prey were rather larger than the marine. Most were eels between 300 and 500 grams in weight compared to the butterfish, blennies and sea scorpions on the coast, very few of which weighed more than 100 grams.

For other types of prey there are even fewer observations. Otters will sometimes catch waterbirds by swimming under them and grabbing them from below, but I suspect that most are caught while nesting or roosting. Terrestrial prey does not form a major part of the diet but it seems unlikely that otters would hunt small mammals such as mice, rats and voles deliberately although they would undoubtedly kill one if they could get close enough. Rabbits are the species most likely to attract the attention of otters because they often live in colonies and each one would provide a substantial meal. However, an otter would probably be unable to catch a rabbit that was fit unless it was taken unawares. Perhaps otters stalk them and then pounce or they may have to concentrate on very young rabbits or those that are less fit and agile.

Frogs require another hunting strategy and since most are taken either during the spawning or the hibernation period there may even be two strategies. They can be so numerous at spawning sites that one imagines that otters can walk along practically grazing on them at the water's edge. During hibernation the frogs hide in the mud at the bottom of small bodies of water when otters must search for them by feel.

WHAT DO OTTERS EAT?

There are no prizes for answering 'otters eat fish', but possibly a consolation prize for following up the answer with further questions such as, 'What sort of fish do they eat?' 'What else do they eat?' 'How much do they eat?' All these questions interest ecologists and some of them interest fishermen as well, so it is not surprising that a great deal of effort has been put into studying the diet of otters.

In order to answer questions like these you need to have suitable techniques for studying the diet. There are three available, each with its own advantages and disadvantages: direct observation, gut content analysis and spraint analysis.

There is a great deal of anecdotal evidence about what otters eat, based on observations of them catching or eating fish, but the problem is that people are much more likely to notice, and make a note of, otters

Eels are a favoured food.

eating large or valuable fish such as salmon and trout than small but possibly more frequently eaten ones like eels or sticklebacks. As otters are largely nocturnal throughout much of Britain the only substantial body of data on their diet based on direct observations comes from the coasts of Scotland, particularly Shetland, where they forage during the day. Here, over a period of four years, Hans Kruuk and his colleagues observed 13,300 otter dives which resulted in 3,585 prey captures. They were able to identify fifty-eight per cent of the prey caught and also to estimate the length of the prey by comparison with the size of the otter's head. This could then be converted to weight of prey consumed.

Analysis of the contents of guts is a messy business but it can be fairly easy to identify the size and type of prey if digestion has not proceeded far. The biggest problem is acquiring dead otters and this technique has only successfully been used in areas where otters have been hunted for their fur, such as North America, Scandinavia and Russia. As hunting for fur is seasonal (the fur is best in winter) and otters are killed over a wide area, it has limited value even there.

In recent years in Britain an increasing number of otters have been killed on the roads and many of these have been collected for post-mortem analysis. Although information on diet can be obtained from such sources, compared to spraints, relatively few samples can be obtained each year and they cover a very wide area. For these reasons no substantial attempt has been made to use them as a means to study otter diet.

By contrast, spraints are reasonably easy to collect and are, effectively, a renewable resource. Collecting them does not harm individual otters and it is possible to build up large collections by regular and diligent searching. For example, over a period of two years, Sam Erlinge collected 15,000 in various parts of Sweden, giving him a very detailed picture of the diet in different areas and throughout the year.

Spraints contain the indigestible remains of recent meals and, provided you can recognise the fragments, it is very easy to work out what they have been eating. It is less simple, however, to determine the relative quantities. Since fish do indeed form the bulk of it, the first need when studying otters' diet is to collect samples of fish from the locality, remove the flesh and make a collection of representative bones. Vertebrae and scales are the most frequently encountered remains but various other typical bones can also be added to the reference collection. It is then a simple matter (in theory at least) to compare the fragments in the spraint with those in the collection. In practice, there are always many bits which are impossible to identify and, generally speaking, the fewer species of fish available to otters, the fewer unidentifiable remains you will be left with, because there is less opportunity for confusion. There is in fact a key to remains in otter spraints published by The Mammal Society (see *Further Reading*).

Once you have identified the remains, you still have to quantify your findings and this is less straightforward. Some prey will have a very high ratio of indigestible matter to meat, crabs and crayfish for example while others will produce few remains in the spraint. Even similar types of prey contribute differently to the spraint contents. Eels, for example, contain about half as much indigestible matter as trout. There are various ways to overcome this, using so called 'correction factors', calculated to enable you to estimate the original proportions of different prey in the diet. In practice they are time-consuming to use and most people use a simple formula based on the number of times a particular type of prey occurs in the spraints. This method, known as 'frequency of occurrence', can lead to an overestimation of the importance of small prey such as sticklebacks if they are eaten regularly or of prey with a high proportion of indigestible remains such as crayfish or crabs. However, provided this is borne in mind, frequency of occurrence gives a useful guide to the diet.

What sort of fish?

Otters living in freshwater generally take whatever fish are most readily available whether they be sticklebacks, trout, roach, perch or eels. However, where there is a choice, there seems to be a tendency for them to take disproportionate numbers of certain types of fish, particularly those that are easier to catch. On the whole they will concentrate on the slower-swimming coarse fish, particularly eels if they can. However, in many places this is not possible and, on the Dartmoor streams where I first studied otter diets, sixty per cent of the remains in spraint were salmonid fish, mainly trout and salmon parr. On the other hand, a further thirty per cent were eels, despite the fact they were quite scarce in the river. Several hundred miles away, in a loch in north-east Scotland, David Jenkins and his colleagues found that eels were the most frequently eaten item for much of the year, usually occurring in more than eighty-five per cent of spraints each month.

Apart from being slower moving than other species, eels are also a very fatty fish which is beneficial in terms of diet, though it has a disadvantage when the environment is polluted with some types of toxic chemical (pesticides or PCBs, for example). These compounds dissolve easily in fat and tend to accumulate, leading to the risk of high concentrations being passed on to fish predators (see *Decline and Fall*, page 115).

Despite some evidence of a preference for slower-moving coarse fish when available, if nothing else is present otters will concentrate on salmonid fish, though taking mainly small ones below the size when they become interesting to anglers.

Some species seem to be overlooked by otters. I found that pike were taken very infrequently by otters in one of my study areas except during their spawning season. This may be because their habit of lying in wait for their prey amongst the water weeds, rather than swimming round after it, makes them less conspicuous to otters than some other species of fish. This protection is lost during the spawning season when the more vigorous activities of courtship bring them to the otters' attention. Similarly in Sweden, tench, which tend to be found in dense vegetation, were rarely caught.

Catchability is also the key for coastal otters. Three-quarters of the fish eaten by otters in Hans Kruuk's study area consisted of four types: eelpout, rocklings, sea scorpion and butterfish. All of these are bottom-dwelling fish and slower moving than species that live in mid-water. In fact free-swimming fish such as saithe and pollack were not commonly eaten (less than eight per cent of the diet between them), although otters did find them a useful source of food in winter when rough seas forced them to hunt in the sheltered parts of the coast favoured by these species.

What size of fish?

There are some accounts of otters killing pike of nine or ten kilograms in weight but it seems unlikely that they would take fish much larger than these since they exceed the weight of the average male otter.

In my study area, on the edge of Dartmoor, only seven per cent of the salmonid fish in the spraints were more than 25 cm long and fifty-eight per cent were less than half this length, reflecting the fact that there are a lot more small fish than large ones available in the river. Nevertheless very tiny fish are probably ignored unless they are particularly abundant or nothing else is available. Thus on the rivers Dee and Don in northern Scotland where otters also eat mainly salmonid fish, they take disproportionate numbers of specimens which are two or three years old (and about 12–16 cm long) compared to the more numerous but less rewarding smaller fish.

In a study of the size of prey at Slapton Ley in south Devon, Margaret Kennedy found a close correspondence between fish size in the otter's diet and the sizes of fish caught in traps, in nets and by electrofishing. However, all these techniques catch fewer of the smallest fish because they can slip through the netting. Margaret found that most fish taken by otters were in the range 6–18 cm and few of the roach, perch or salmonid fish eaten exceeded this. Eels tended to be somewhat larger, however, mainly in the region of 20–40 cm in one area and 10–35 cm in another, while

the largest eel taken was 70 cm long. Otters also took large specimens of pike. Nearly half the pike eaten exceeded 50 cm in length and one (out of 274) was more than 80 cm long. A 50-cm pike would weigh a little under two kilos, more than enough to feed an otter for a day, and an 80-cm pike would weigh about five kilos.

In Shetland too, otters seemed to deliberately select larger than average prey since the average weight of fish eaten was about twice that of fish caught in traps. Even so, nearly half the fish eaten by otters weighed less than fifty grams and were less than 13 cm in length. Some were less than ten grams in weight while at the other extreme, those exceeding one hundred grams constituted about fifteen per cent of the diet.

Does the diet vary through the year?

As otters tend to concentrate on the most catchable prey, and prey behaviour varies through the year, it is hardly surprising that, where there is a choice, the diet varies too. In the case of fish it is activity and distribution which have the greatest effect. Eels, for example, tend to burrow into the mud in winter where they are hard for otters to find, so they are usually taken most frequently in the summer. More active fish such as roach and salmonids are easier to catch in the winter when the water is colder and the fish swim more slowly. Migration is also important and otters are obviously only able to feed on salmon and sea-trout while they are in the rivers.

Similarly in large lakes and on the coast fish may migrate to and from the shoreline at different times of year and in both cases they are taken more frequently by otters when they are abundant near the shore.

Another activity which increases the chances of fish being taken by otters is spawning. Species which spawn in shallow water often increase dramatically in the otter's diet during the breeding season. This is particularly so for species which have limited spawning beds and gather in large concentrations resulting in a great deal of activity which attracts the otters. No doubt the minds of the fish are concentrated on their nuptials rather than the risk of predation.

Studies in Scotland showed that, although some otters regularly take adult salmon when the fish are in the rivers for spawning, predation falls mainly on male fish and particularly those which had finished spawning and were in very poor condition.

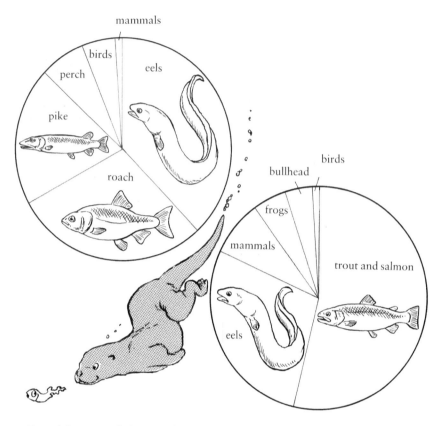

Typical diet in two habitats: a dartmoor stream (right) and a lowland lake (left).

What else do they eat?

In most studies of otters' diets which cover the full year, fish make up between sixty-five and ninety per cent of the items recognised. In the few cases where fish formed less than sixty-five per cent of the diet, otters were feeding extensively on crayfish and/or frogs as well. However, like most carnivores, otters will eat whatever they can get and a surprising array of other items have been recorded. Here, I will concentrate mainly on the significant ones.

Invertebrates: Crayfish, crabs and water beetles are the only types of invertebrate to occur regularly in otter spraint and only crayfish ever form a substantial part of the diet. Interestingly, people who have studied the diet of coastal otters by looking at spraint have found that as much as twenty per cent of the diet consists of crabs. However, there is an awful lot of indigestible skeleton in a crab and only three per cent of the captures observed by Hans Kruuk and his colleagues were of crab. Since crabs are fairly easy to recognise and only have a small amount of flesh, even this may over-emphasize their importance in the diet. Rocklings provide over four times as much energy for a given effort as do crabs, and butterfish about three times as much so, if an otter can catch them, it is more worth while to do so. Sometimes, of course, rocklings and butterfish may be scarce and crabs common so the otter must take what it can get but on the whole crabs, though easier to capture, provide a poor rate of return on the energy invested in getting them.

Crayfish also contain a lot of hard parts but they undoubtedly form a substantial part of the otter's diet in some places. On one river in Sweden their remains were found in eighty per cent of spraints collected from June to August and, in parts of the river Clare system in County Galway, Eire, all scats collected during the summer contained crayfish. At all but one site in Galway crayfish contributed between sixty and eighty-five per cent of the prey remains collected between July and December. Even so, because they have such a high proportion of shell to flesh, their contribution to the otter's nutrition must be considerably lower than this. In Portugal, Pedro Beja found that otters consumed considerable numbers of an introduced species, the American red swamp crayfish. Nearly twenty per cent of the energy requirements of otters were supplied by these aliens which the otters seem to catch particularly frequently when they were hunting for eels whose habitat they shared.

Amphibia: Otters living near marshy areas often consume large numbers of frogs. This seems to occur at two seasons, during hibernation and during the breeding season. At other times frogs are mainly found away from water and are much less prominent in the diet. Where frogs are reasonably common they may form as much as twenty per cent of the diet over the year but in winter and spring may reach as much as fifty per cent of the items identified in some areas. Otters seem to know where frogs hibernate and search for them in those areas. Judging from my own pond, the vigorous and noisy activity at the spawning sites must make it very easy for otters to find them.

Toads are hardly ever eaten. In Scotland one study showed that of 150 spraints containing amphibian remains only four were toads. This is not necessarily because toads are rarer than frogs but may be because they have glands in their skin which make them distasteful.

Some otters have learned how to overcome this and an international incident was narrowly averted a few years ago after discarded amphibian skins were found near a pond in Cumbria. It was first thought that someone had been taking frogs for the French restaurant trade until it was realised that not only were these toad skins but also that there were otter footprints around the pond. One otter had learned how to remove the distasteful skin to get at the juicy flesh inside.

There are no records of newts being eaten by otters but they are, of course, rather small and not very common. In addition their remains may be hard to detect in spraints.

Reptiles: In many places where people have studied the diet of otters, reptiles are not recorded at all but they are eaten more frequently in southern Europe. In one area in Italy snake remains were second only in importance to fish in the diet. A high proportion of reptile remains were from the genus Natrix. Sometimes known as water snakes, and including the grass snake, these animals often feed in or near water. I suppose a snake is much like an eel to an otter but it would be interesting to know whether they were caught on land or in the water. These snakes are also fond of frogs so perhaps otters found them while both were seeking that prey.

Birds: Waterbirds are the most frequent avian prey, particularly coots, moorhens and ducks. Although otters are capable of taking adult birds, predation is usually concentrated on the young and these birds tend to be taken most frequently in summer. Two surprising species featuring in the diet in some areas are swallows and starlings. The reason for this appears to be their habit of roosting in reeds, sometimes in tens or even hundreds of thousands. Starlings do so in the winter and swallows (and martins) during their spring and autumn migrations. Whether otters catch healthy birds or simply pick up dead and dying birds as they travel through the reed beds is not known.

Mammals: Otters would probably eat any small mammal if they could catch it but they are not well designed for hunting voles, mice and rats, so when they do occur in the diet it is probably as an incidental extra rather than the result of deliberate searching and hunting. No doubt most species of small mammals have been eaten at one time or another but only two species turn up more than occasionally – rabbits and water voles. Water voles probably because they live along the river bank, sometimes at quite high densities, and are therefore more likely to be encountered than other small mammals. Rabbits are sizable prey making a good meal for an otter and may be quite abundant although they do not necessarily live close to water. They are the one type of terrestrial (as opposed to waterside) prey it is worthwhile for otters to hunt so it is not surprising that one radio-tagged female otter in Shetland frequently ate rabbits, catching them in their burrows. I am sure many others do the same.

Carrion: There has been some debate as to whether otters feed on carrion or not. Attempts to persuade them to take bait marked with dyes or small pieces of plastic (which might show up in the faeces) have usually failed, although a recent effort to tempt them with sprats did work, and was recorded by an infrared camera.

Sam Erlinge found that otters in Sweden often ate bream which had died after being caught by fishermen and thrown away and I have seen the remains of a large pike which seemed to have been consumed entirely by otters probably over a couple of days or more.

In a study in 1995 of scavenging on salmon Ray Hewson marked a number of salmon carcasses with radio-tags and followed their movements as they were washed downstream recording their consumption by various predators on the way. Apart from providing his friends with a good source of material for teasing ('Were you really radio-tracking dead salmon?'), Ray found that otters were important in this process. This was partly because they kill large salmon and leave them on the bank where other predators can feed on them and also because they retrieve the carcasses of salmon from within the water with the same result. Hewson was not always able to clearly distinguish between salmon killed by otters and then eaten and salmon retrieved by otters when dead but he had good evidence of otters feeding on salmon that were already dead, indicating that carrion feeding by otters was a regular occurrence in his study area.

How much do they eat?
It is virtually impossible to find this out from wild otters but in captivity male otters seem to need about 1.5 kg per day. This suggests that the average male otter would consume a little over half a tonne of food in a year. It seems a formidable amount! Before fishermen reach for their guns or traps, however, it is worth bearing in mind the large distances otter travel in search of their food. On an upland river containing mainly trout and salmon, they might travel several kilometres in a night and have a home range extending over tens of kilometres. On the basis of a modest-sized range on such a river, say 40 km, a male otter would only need to find 1.25 kg per year from each hundred metres, of river – a much less worrying figure.

Foraging along the strand line.

Eclectic tastes

One book on the carnivores suggested they will eat 'whatever they can get' and there is a great deal of truth in the notion. Some things are easier to 'get' than others as different carnivores are adapted to catching different prey and a hungry carnivore is likely to be less fussy about what it eats than a satiated one. On the whole, however, it is a carnivore's specialisation in hunting techniques that determines the main items in its diet while chance and circumstances dictate what other items may be eaten from time to time.

It is not too surprising then to find that if you look at the whole range of food eaten by otters it is a very long list with some rather odd items in it. The strangest is a cuckoo's egg but, as this was reputedly eaten by Tarka in Henry Williamson's book, it may owe more to his imagination than to observation. While eggs may not often feature on the otter's menu, birds certainly do and a remarkable variety of them too. Blackbird, dipper, grouse and wagtail have been reported as well as various species of wading and swimming birds. I always thought that the small songbirds eaten by otters were taken as carrion until I read of a report in *The Naturalist* in 1923 of an otter catching a live sparrow. As the otter launched its attack from a distance of more than two metres, it must have been a very dozy sparrow.

The remains of insects (and some other freshwater invertebrates) occur quite often in otter spraints but these usually accompany fish remains, leading to the conclusion that they were eaten by the fish which had been eaten by the otter. Water beetles do turn up in spraints in quite large numbers from time to time indicating that the otters have caught them deliberately, possibly actively searching them out. Large terrestrial insects such as dung beetles were 'greedily devoured' by some tame otters but I would never have expected the burrowing mole cricket to be at risk from otter predation. In the Doñana National Park in south-west Spain, however, it is. My *Collins Guide to Insects* says that mole crickets live in moist meadows, especially near rivers. This may partly explain it, but I do not know whether the otters dig for the crickets or catch them at the entrances to their burrows where they indulge in a 'long periods of quiet churring' presumably for courtship purposes.

If they eat mole crickets, then why not moles? Considering their subterranean habits, moles turn up surprisingly regularly in the otter's diet, albeit at a very low level. Moles are in fact good swimmers, quite capable of crossing ditches and probably small rivers as well. They are eaten by herons too, mainly when the young disperse from their mother's range.

Slugs and snails would be difficult to detect in spraints although the remains of earthworms have been found in stomachs of dead otters, and tame otters will certainly take slugs. However, there is some dissension about whether or not otters will eat that large freshwater mollusc, the swan mussel. Most reports are based on finding the remains of a meal rather than seeing otters eat them but one person measured the distance between teeth marks on mussel shells and found that they were similar to the gap between otter canine teeth which is suggestive if not conclusive. On the other hand captive otters seem quite unable to tackle mussels, playing with them like pebbles without opening them, although willing to eat the contents if the shells are broken for them. It may be that the mussel-eating habit is passed from mother to cub, so that young otters reared in captivity which have not had the opportunity to learn that the shells contain a tasty morsel do not acquire the habit.

OTTERS AND THEIR PREY

Many people believe that animal populations are 'controlled' by predation. Recognising that a predator may consume large numbers of any one species of prey, they think that if it stops feeding on that species the numbers will increase uncontrollably. This is often used as justification for the introduction of another method of 'control' such as hunting, shooting or trapping. Sometimes this is indeed the case but in fact it is quite often the other way round – the abundance of the prey determines the abundance of the predator. We should not be too surprised therefore to find that although the otter used to be blamed for clearing streams of fish, especially trout, there is no evidence for this.

A few people have tried to estimate the impact of otter predation on populations of their prey and have come up with some interesting statistics. Sam Erlinge estimated the consumption of fish by otters on a lake in Sweden as being about 1.6 tonne per year whereas fishermen were taking over 3 tonne. Fishermen took one and a half to two times as many cyprinid fish (carp family) as otters and seven to ten times as many eels and pike. Other predators included herons, grebes and mergansers, plus the fish themselves. Sam calculated that the pike in the lake probably consumed more fish than man and otters combined. In spite of all this piscivory, he concluded that the fish population in the lake could only be increased by increasing the food available to the fish not by reducing predation.

In the stream flowing from this lake the crayfish population was also heavily exploited by otters and fishermen, and Erlinge calculated that between them they removed about half the crayfish each year, otters catching two for every three taken by fishermen. Here, too, the prey population was able to withstand the onslaught because enough crayfish grew to catchable size each year to replace those removed. Of course, if the fishermen had increased their catch, perhaps by using more efficient methods of catching the crayfish, this might indeed have led to a reduction in prey availability for the otter.

Hans Kruuk tried to estimate the impact of otter predation on populations of fish on the coast of Shetland. He was only able to do so for one species, the five-bearded rockling, partly because it was confined to the zone in which otters fished and partly because it was present all

Alert otter

year round and was easily caught in his fish traps. He concluded that, on average, in each kilometre of coast there were 2,600 rocklings and each year the otters took about a quarter of these, mainly the larger specimens. Again, the population of rocklings did not decline from year to year so it was clearly able to withstand this level of attack. No doubt if man suddenly discovered a penchant for five-bearded rocklings and an easy way to catch them, things might be different. On a smaller scale, Hans also found that by intensive trapping he could catch all the fish in a patch of weed covering a few square metres but that it would be re-colonised within twenty-four hours.

Elsewhere in Scotland, on the rivers Dee and Don, Hans and his colleagues calculated that otters ate more than half the annual production of salmonid fish in some streams. This does not necessarily mean that they were damaging the fishing. Most of the prey were under 20 cm in length and if otter predation were to be removed the fish might compete for food and grow more slowly or to a smaller size.

In fact, studies in Shetland and mainland Scotland have shown that otters are 'limited' by their food supply to the extent that, when fish numbers declined, so did the otters. This is partly because otters cannot find enough food, so their condition declines, which leads to more deaths, but also because their breeding is affected. In poor years for fish, fewer cubs are born than when the fishing is good. Between 2003 and 2009 the otter population of Shetland is believed to have declined by about fifty per cent and this has been attributed to a decline in fish populations. Evidence to support this comes from the observation that otters ate increasing numbers of crabs in this period, prey which is much less nutritious.

These observations also reinforce the fact that otters live a precarious existence needing to balance carefully the energy they use to find and catch food with the energy they obtain from it. To misquote Mr Micawber:

'Energy income 2,000 calories, energy expenditure 1,995 calories, result life. Energy income 2,000 calories, energy expenditure 2,005 calories, result death.'

A similar pattern was observed by Jordi Ruiz-Olmo in Spain. There, rivers may be affected by seasonal drought when some dry up leaving only pools of water in the river bed, or by severe flooding which sweeps away much of the river bed and the fish with it. He too found higher mortality and lower breeding success when food supplies were poor.

Under these circumstances, it is not surprising to find that on the coast, where food is more abundant, otter populations are at a higher density than inland. Similarly, on rivers in northern Spain, Jordi Ruiz-Olmo found that more otters used the stretches which had more fish.

What eats otters?

As with their prey, there is still a popular notion that otters 'need' a predator to control their numbers and people often ask me what their natural predators are. Of course, there are none in Britain, probably never have been.

Like other fierce carnivores, otters are well able to fight off most of the predators that live in their environment. Throughout much of their range the only predators large enough to attack them successfully would be bears, wolves or wolverines (a larger mustelid) and there are no records of any of these doing so.

In general, although larger carnivorous mammals do occasionally kill and eat smaller ones, this happens very rarely. This is partly because other prey is much more abundant and also easier to subdue. It has also been suggested that carnivore flesh may be less palatable than other prey. Experiments with tame foxes showed that they would turn up their noses at weasel and badger meat even when they were hungry enough to eat voles and mice.

Photographs by
LAURIE CAMPBELL

Having grown up living close to the river Tweed by my home town of Berwick-upon-Tweed in the Scottish Borders, I feel I've known this river and its tributaries and the wildlife they contain for over forty years. I just never imagined that one day I might have the chance of seeing otters, let alone photograph them in my own backyard.

It wasn't until the late 1980s that I first started seeing tell-tale signs marking their return to our local rivers. The odd footprint on a muddy river bank and spraint on rocks came well before my first sighting. Over the years I've noticed a gradual change in otter behaviour where they have become progressively more tolerant to limited disturbance and this has coincided with the steady increase in their numbers. I've also seen an increasing tendency for them to be active in daylight too, sometimes even in the middle of the day. At the same time the advent of digital photography, and particularly the capability of cameras to function in marginal lighting, has at last offered greater possibilities for photographing otters. From slow beginnings, I'm now finding that I can predictably obtain sightings of otters at least thirty per cent of the time I go looking for them and, because it's all conveniently been happening on my doorstep, I've been able to amass many hundreds of hours in the field, observing and photographing them.

The notes on each image are by the author, Paul Chanin.

A good profile of an otter's head. Notice that the eyes and ears are rather small but the nostrils comparatively large. This otter is swimming steadily at the surface in a horizontal posture, whiskers swept back.
Loch Seaforth, Harris.

Another profile but this otter has an upright posture and is either floating or treading water. It is very alert and looking to see what is happening. River Teviot, Roxburghshire.

Feeding on a small fish. Notice the sharp piercing teeth at the front for holding wriggling prey. Those at the back are also sharp but designed for slicing. As well as whiskers on the muzzle, the ones at the side of the face are clearly visible.
River Teviot, Roxburghshire.

Top.
When the water is shallow, otters will walk along the bottom and, where it is steep and fast flowing, a streamlined shape helps. So does the equivalent of four-wheel drive – broad spreading feet.
River Teviot, Roxburghshire.

Bottom.
The beginning of a steep dive. The otter has thrust itself up out of the water in order to gain momentum for a dive in deeper water. The faster it goes down, the longer it can stay there.
River Teviot, Roxburghshire.

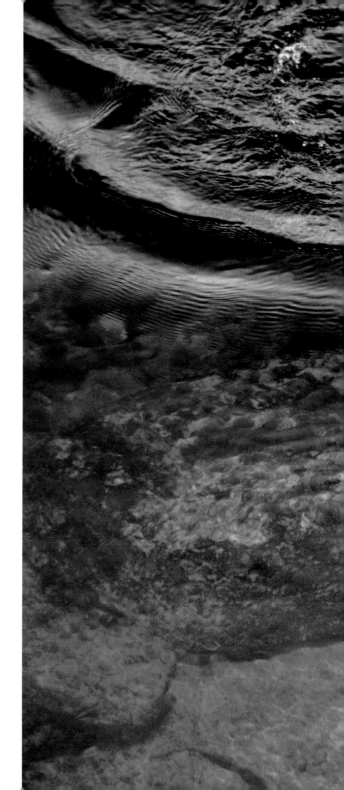

*The start of a shallow dive.
Notice the upwelling from
a powerful thrust of the
hind end of the body and
legs – out to the side. You
can see a wave travelling
along the tail. Forelimbs
are tucked into the body
to minimise drag. Bubbles
rise to the surface as they
are squeezed out of the fur.
River Teviot,
Roxburghshire.*

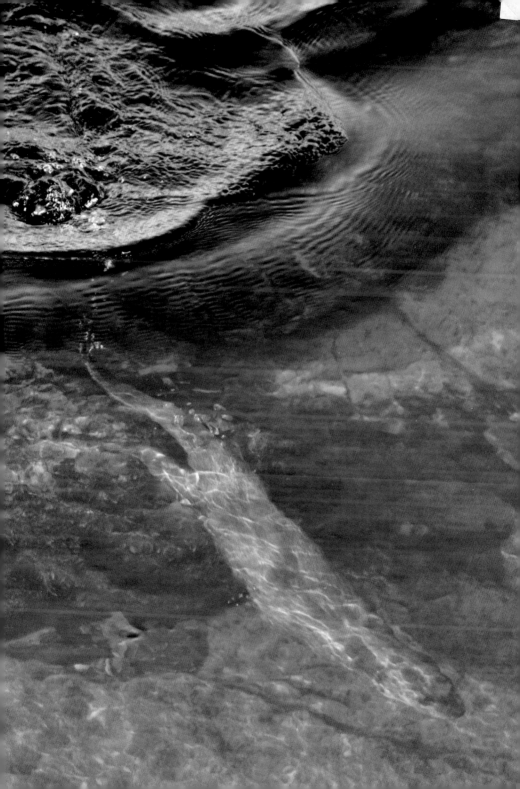

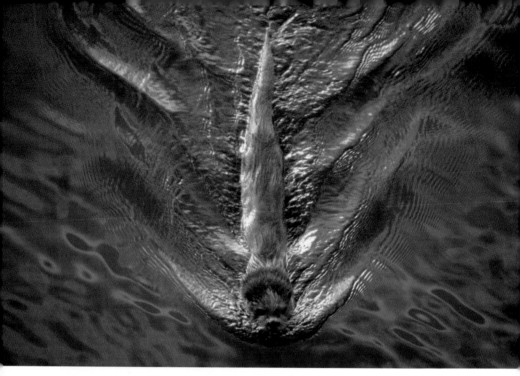

Top.
Otters can swim faster under water but at the surface a brisk pace creates a substantial wake, with the back visible above water.
River Tweed.

Left.
Otters are largely solitary. When you see more than one together it is usually a family group. Fighting between adults occurs only occasionally but play fighting is not unusual between young otters.
River Teviot, Roxburghshire.

Above.
Two very young cubs who have clearly been swimming, perhaps for the first time. The anxious looks may be because the mother has left them at the water's edge in an effort to encourage them to follow her. River Whiteadder, Berwickshire.

Right.
A cub this large probably dives with its mother and is beginning to catch its own food. Nevertheless it follows her closely, perhaps benefiting from her wake. River Teviot, Roxburghshire.

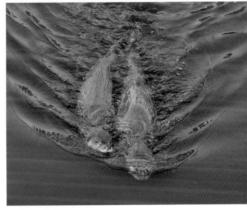

Left.
As the cubs grow they follow their mother when foraging, staying as close to her as they can. By this stage they will be eating solid food. Broadford Bay, Skye.

The average size of family groups declines with age as mortality is higher in the first year of life than the second. This cub (nearer camera) will soon reach adult size, be able to fend for itself and perhaps be 'persuaded' by its mother to leave home. River Teviot, Roxburghshire.

Above.
This view is quite characteristic, particularly in coastal otters. Small prey is consumed in the water with rapid movements of the head as it is manipulated between the jaws and sliced up into bite-sized chunks.
River Teviot, Roxburghshire.

Above right.
Eels are fairly manageable and quite large ones can be eaten in the water, held by the forepaws and eaten like a stick of rock.
River Tweed.

Below right.
This salmon is more than one meal's worth for an otter. It will be left on the shore and the otter may return to feast on it further – if someone else doesn't get there first.
River Whiteadder, Berwickshire.

Large prey is taken to the shore, either when feeding young or because it is too difficult to handle in the water.
Broadford Bay, Skye.

Laurie Campbell has dedicated over thirty-five years to photographing Scotland's distinctive wildlife and flora. After graduating from a four-year degree course in photography at Napier University he continued accumulating stocks of photographs of wildlife and in 1985 became Scotland's first full-time professional nature photographer. His imagery is published across a range of media and is widely recognised

The photographer: Laurie Campbell

for its distinctive style and his preference for using natural light and belief in photographing subjects which are neither captive nor manipulated but simply as he finds them in the field.

Laurie's experience in photography means he is in constant demand as a lecturer and photographic workshop leader, both in the UK and throughout Europe. He is also valued as a photographic judge and has been invited onto the panel for the prestigious *BBC Wildlife Photographer of the Year*, a competition in which he has previously won twenty-three awards.

More of Laurie's images can be seen on his website: www.lauriecampbell.com

OTTER MOVEMENTS AND ACTIVITIES

Although otters are highly aquatic animals it would be a mistake to think that they spend the bulk of their time in water. In fact otters spend as much as seventy per cent of their time in their dens and even when 'active' outside their dens they spend quite a bit of time resting.

The otters radio-tracked by Jim and Rosemary Green tended to have two or three periods of activity, resting between these. The male was most energetic and spent about sixty per cent of the night on the move and forty per cent resting. These otters left their dens around sunset and were most active in the following three to five hours. This was usually followed by another bout of activity late in the night before they settled down for the day around dawn. Occasionally they came out during the day but not very often.

This nocturnal pattern seems to be typical of otters on rivers generally but it is very different from those living on the coast which are active during the day and hardly ever by night. It has always been believed that this was a reflection of the different levels of disturbance in the two habitats but Hans Kruuk has suggested that this may not be so. He pointed out that the species of coastal fish eaten most frequently by otters are inactive during the daytime, hiding under stones and in weeds, and suggests that they may be easier for otters to find at this time. Maybe the otter has a better chance of catching a fish which has just been dozing than an active one. Apparently several species of freshwater fish also have periods of inactivity when they settle to the bottom and may be more vulnerable to otters. These species rest at night so perhaps that is why inland otters are active then. On the other hand, eels are active at night and they are certainly a regular item on the otter's menu. Perhaps some species are easier to catch when they are resting (fast swimming species, for example) while other, slower-moving fish such as eels, are easier to catch when they are active. We still have a lot to learn.

In recent years I have heard several reports of otters being active during the daytime on rivers. I even saw one, once, forging upstream at 10.30 in the morning where I was doing an otter survey. One or two people have suggested that this shows a change in their activity patterns compared to earlier years. As I was at primary school when the otter was last widespread in Britain I have nothing to compare with, and there are not many people who are as likely to have observed otters fifty years ago as today. If there is a real difference, rather than a perceived one, it might be that otters are now more willing to be active during the day because they are no longer hunted. More likely, perhaps, that otters have always occasionally come out during the daytime.

Coastal otters have fairly short bouts of hunting, averaging about a quarter of an hour before they come out of the water. They then groom and rest for about the same length of time before returning to the hunt. This may be connected with their body temperatures. Despite their thick fur, otters cool down while in the water, and they need to have a regular break in which they can warm up and restore the insulating layer of air to their underfur.

As well as being active for longer periods, male otters travel further and a little faster than females, although the actual distances in both sexes vary considerably between nights and between different areas. In Sweden Sam Erlinge recorded an average distance of 9 km per night for male otters while females varied from 3 km to 7 km depending on whether they were accompanied by cubs and the age of the cubs. Needless to say they do not move in straight lines. Jim and Rosemary Green calculated the distances between successive daytime resting places and found that they averaged approximately 4 km for the male and 2 km for the females. Actual distances travelled were considerably greater, the longest distance in one night being 16 km covered by the male, a remarkable feat for such a short-legged animal. Even so, he ended up a mere 3 km from his starting place.

The fastest movements were usually only recorded for short distances, for example one female managed 500 m in ten minutes (3 km per hour). However, on one occasion, the male achieved a speed of 4.4 km per hour over a distance of 9 km although he was going downstream with a spate behind him so this record was 'current-assisted'.

Not only is there a difference in the extent and speed of movements between the sexes but also in their nature. Female otters tend to travel straight to one of a few favoured foraging areas and then move to and fro in a zig-zag pattern presumably searching for food. Males, on the other hand, spend much more time in travelling and rather little in diligently searching for food, perhaps feeding while on the move. They spend much more time than the females in examining the boundaries of their ranges and make forays to every part of it. In both Scotland and Sweden it seems as though the males set off on regular patrols around their range which last for four or five days.

During their travels otters may use regular routes and paths. In fact, in Sweden it turns out that the routes they follow when walking across the lake ice in winter are the same as the ones they swim across in the summer. They will quite frequently take short cuts across land, particularly when travelling upstream along a meandering stream, or from one body of water to another. Well-worn trails develop which can be quite easily recognised. I have seen paths in the Outer Hebrides which look like badger trails or even narrow human paths. However, there are no badgers in the Hebrides and the trails went from one waterbody to another and had otter spraints at intervals along them making it clear whose feet had trodden them.

Otters seem to cross from one watershed to another quite readily. One killed on a Norfolk road, miles from the nearest river, seemed to have travelled along small brooks to a point where it had a relatively short

Running up a freshwater stream.

journey to make across land between the rivers Bure and Wensum. Even so it still had to walk nearly 2 km across country to make the connection. Another Norfolk otter, released as part of the re-introduction scheme in the area, managed to find its way to an isolated gravel pit across 400 m of ploughed field.

In south-west England, records of otters killed on the road show that this is quite often at a place where there is no stream under the road, but where the road runs along the watershed. Many otters seem to have lost their lives when passing from one catchment to another.

TERRITORY AND LIVING SPACE

Most mammals have a fairly well-defined area in which they carry out their day-to-day activities and this is known as their home range. If you track an animal over a period of time it is usually possible to work out where the normal boundaries of its range lie. It may make the occasional excursion outside them but spends most of its life in a familiar area in which it knows its way around and where to find the good feeding places and the safe dens and resting places.

Some animals actively try to exclude other members of the same species (or sometimes just the same sex) by defending their range. This is known as territoriality. Defence does not always have to be by physical aggression, of course. There are many other ways of warning off intruders. Many birds and some mammals use song or other vocal calls but a much more subtle method is to use scent which has the great advantage of not needing

The evening sun on Mull.

the owner's presence. Rather like a sign which says 'Trespassers will be Prosecuted', it gives a warning without the territory owner having to be there and, unlike singing, howling or roaring, it will last for a reasonable period of time. On the other hand, scent marks do need to be backed up by at least the possibility of the intruder being caught in the act. Thus it pays territory holders to patrol their territories regularly keeping an eye out for intruders and also making sure that the signs are still legible, i.e. renewing the scent marks.

There are many problems over territoriality, both for the animals trying to implement it as a strategy and for biologists trying to study them. For example, although territorial birds can usually fly from one side of their territory to the other very quickly and see off any intruders, it is much more difficult for mammals, many of which have rather short legs in relation to the distances they may have to travel across their territory. The result of this is that intruders are more likely to get away with an incursion into a resident mammal's territory. The trespasser might be an itinerant animal 'just passing through' but it could also be a neighbouring territory holder. If some animals do intrude in this way, how can the biologist be sure that the range really is defended?

To some extent this does not matter. Although it is convenient for us to divide animals into those that are territorial and those that are not, there is no reason why the animals should fit into the neat categories we make for them or even into the same category everywhere they live. Nevertheless, people do like to organise things into neat little pigeon-holes – well, I do anyway – and the fact that otters are so adaptable in their behaviour has made this one of the hardest chapters to write. If at the end of this chapter you feel slightly confused about otter territoriality, please blame the otters. I feel the same.

Home range size
For most mammals the size of the range is expressed as an area but otter ranges are often measured as lengths, usually of river or coastline. This is a very simple and convenient way of showing how far an otter may have to travel to get from one end of its range to another but it does make comparisons difficult. For example, lakes and marshes are often very important feeding areas for otters but they are best measured in

terms of area. Also, measuring the length of a home range on a river takes no account of the width or depth, each of which would have significant effects on food availability.

Sam Erlinge studied home ranges in Sweden in two areas consisting of series of lakes connected by streams. He followed the otters' movements by tracking them in snow and distinguished two main categories by their footprints: males, which had large prints, and family groups, consisting of medium-sized and small footprints. (Medium-sized footprints on their own could have been females without cubs or young males.) Most otters had part or all of at least one lake in their ranges and all included some stream. The streams were evidently essential to the otters since in the winter the lakes freeze over and fishing is restricted to flowing water. Females with cubs had home ranges of about 6 or 7 km except for one family group which had no lake within its range and travelled along 10–12 km of stream. Males had much larger ranges between 10 and 20 km in length with an average of 15 km.

Jim and Rosemary Green's study area, the river Earn near Perth in Scotland, had only one substantial loch in it, and their otters had much larger home ranges. The two females had ranges of 16 km and 22 km while the male ranged over approximately 40 km of river and stream. In more recent studies carried out on the rivers Dee and Don in the north of Scotland male home ranges were very variable (between 12 and 80 km of river) while two females' ranges covered about 20 km of water.

Coastal otters in Scotland generally have smaller ranges than those inland, typically stretching along 2 to 10 km of shore, although some exceed this and, as on inland waters, males have larger ranges than females. In Shetland two female ranges which were well known included 4.7 km and 6.4 km of shoreline while another, where the boundaries were less well known, stretched along about 14 km of the coast. The largest known range of an animal resident in that area was of an adult male who travelled along 19.3 km of the coast. At the other extreme some coastal otters can find all their needs in a remarkably small area; a female tracked by Jane Twelves had a home range only 500 metres in diameter. However, there was probably a considerable length of shore line within this, owing to the convoluted nature of the north-east coast of South Uist.

It is obvious that where the density of fish is high, otter ranges can be smaller and where it is low, such as on unproductive upland streams, they will need to be larger. It is also important to bear in mind that food density is not the determining factor, but availability. Generally speaking the two things go together but there will be places and times where they do not. One such is in Sweden where the lakes freeze over in winter. If they did not, family groups could probably have much smaller territories, confined to the lakes. The need to have access to fishing areas in winter means that they must also include areas of less productive stream in their home range. Even in Scotland, where some otter ranges could be confined to rivers, the need to have somewhere to forage during times of spate may necessitate the inclusion of small streams and areas of marsh in home ranges. Coastal otters too must forage in times of rough seas and storms so they may need to have areas which are sheltered if parts of their range are along exposed coasts. There are also important differences in prey availability between sheltered and exposed coasts in Shetland and otters may gain further benefits by having both sheltered and exposed areas within their ranges. Rocklings and sea scorpions are found in the more exposed areas, throughout the year. However, if otters are to take advantage of the abundance of eelpout during the summer, they must hunt them in more sheltered spots. Likewise in the winter, the sheltered areas are good hunting grounds for pollack and saithe when exposed coasts are buffeted by the weather.

Social relationships

In Sweden most family groups had distinctly separate ranges. In one case there was a small area of overlap but generally there were gaps between the boundaries of family group ranges. This suggests that perhaps the ranges did not extend any further because all the families' needs were encompassed within them, rather than because they would encroach on a neighbour. Dog otters on the other hand had areas of overlap at the boundaries of their ranges, sometimes of three or four kilometres. So, are they territorial?

Erlinge concluded that both males and family groups were territorial in his study area. Although the family groups did not seem to have to defend their boundaries from neighbouring families, there were never two family groups in the same range at once and other otters, apart from adult males, avoided the family ranges. Although male ranges overlapped at the edges, Erlinge had two clear signs of territoriality. First, overlap *only* occurred at the edges. Second, when a resident male was shot in his study area a neighbouring male moved in and took over a substantial part of its range within a week. He also found evidence that there was a dominance hierarchy amongst the male otters. Those nearer the central part of his study area which was most productive seemed to be dominant to those in the peripheral and less productive areas. In the areas of overlap the otters avoided one another, the subordinate otter keeping out of the way or even leaving the area while the dominant one was there.

This arrangement – males and females living solitary lives and holding separate territories – is typical for members of the weasel family. They exclude members of the same sex but territories may overlap with those of one or more members of the opposite sex. However, in some areas a different system prevails.

In Shetland Hans Kruuk and his colleagues found that female otters have group territories, with up to four or five of them using the same range and

Warning off an intruder.

respecting the same boundaries. Within this range they lead quite separate lives. They only meet infrequently and tend to avoid one another when this happens. They use separate dens and also have separate 'core areas', the regions where they spend most of their time. The territory boundaries remained stable over a period of five years despite some otters dying and being replaced. Some boundaries centred on conspicuous features such as streams or stone walls but others occurred where there were none. Intrusions by neighbouring resident females were never observed, but on one occasion, when an unknown, perhaps itinerant, adult female encroached into a territory, she was attacked by a resident.

Hans has suggested that, in this situation, scent marking by resident females could also be of benefit to the otters who share their territories. He noticed that they often sprainted below the tideline which meant that the scent was very quickly washed away. This made it of limited value for territory marking but it could indicate to the other otters in the group that this particular area had recently been fished. A marker which says 'This area has just been fished' could be useful if, by the time of the next tide, food supply had built up again. When he trapped out all the fish in a small area, Hans did find that the population was very quickly replenished so this observation does make sense, particularly if the otters are closely related to one another, as seemed to be the case, since the marking behaviour could benefit daughters, aunts or cousins.

Males had much larger ranges than females and they too overlapped extensively (with other males as well as with females). However, male ranges did not have common boundaries and, when two males met, they usually fought one another. In other words, although the males did not maintain exclusive territories, the groups of females did. Why should this be?

Territories are not defended for their own sake, but for the resources contained within their boundaries. There are three resources which most animals might wish to defend and not share with others of their own kind: food, den sites and mates. In addition, freshwater pools may also be an important resource for coastal otters, not just for drinking but for washing salt from their coats after swimming in the sea. Too many otters sharing the same few pools could lead to the water becoming brackish and less effective.

On the coast, each otter needs to have sufficient lengths of sheltered and exposed coasts within its range to provide sources of food throughout the year, as well as a secure den and a year-round supply of freshwater. The coasts of Shetland are rather 'coarse grained' in that you get long stretches of exposed shores interspersed with long stretches of sheltered water. Both freshwater bathing sites and den sites are found at intervals along the coast so that otters are never more than about 700 metres from either of these. However, in order to have access to all the necessary resources, a female needs to have a home range a few kilometres long. Within her home range, if there is ample food and enough washing and den sites, there is no reason why she should not share with others, particularly if they are her relatives.

A non-territorial system, with overlapping home ranges, would make it impossible to ensure that there was not too much competition for the resources. However, by teaming up into small groups and defending a common territory, the females could ensure that they all had access to the various required resources but still defend them against other animals and thereby prevent over-exploitation. There was some evidence that the otters which shared territories were related to one another. One way such a system could develop is for young females to stay in the home range in which they were born if the resources are sufficient for sharing.

Male otter ranges are larger than females'. It has been suggested that this is because it gives a male the opportunity to mate with more females than he would if he only had a range big enough to provide sufficient food. The number of offspring produced by females is limited by their ability to raise individual litters (which depends to a large extent on the availability of food in their ranges). However, the number of young produced by a male otter during his lifetime depends on the number of females he manages to mate with. As male ranges overlap female ranges, the bigger the male's range the more females he will get the chance to mate with and the more young he will produce.

Many mammals have adaptable social systems which fit in with the prevailing situation, so we should not be surprised to find that otters vary their behaviour to suit the different habitats they exploit.

SOCIAL LIFE AND BEHAVIOUR

Eurasian otters are solitary by nature and probably spend more time avoiding each other's company than seeking it. Even those females which share group ranges in Shetland did not spend time in each other's company. Although the ranges of males and females overlap, there is no 'pairing' and for most of the time the sexes ignore one another. In captivity people have often kept male and female otters together without harm so there appears to be no antagonism between them but, in the wild, mutual avoidance is the norm. This changes during courtship, of course, and for a period of four or five days, while the female is in breeding condition, she will be accompanied by an escort.

Otters courting

Courting

Courtship can be an active and noisy affair. Jim and Rosemary Green were radio-tracking their male otter when he encountered a female and they described his excited behaviour over the next two nights. This included vigorous chasing through the undergrowth, rushing across a road and jumping about on a stone wall together with a great deal of chatter including purring, squeaking, grunting and even crooning. The otters seemed completely unaware of the presence of an observer and even occasional passing cars. This went on for two nights and then, for the following five nights, the male lingered around the female's home range. However, she seemed to want nothing more to do with him and after that he resumed his normal travels. Although these two otters stayed within the female's range, in Sweden Sam Erlinge followed the tracks of a courting pair which travelled a considerable distance together, covering 11 km of waterway, well outside the female's normal range.

The Scottish otters observed by the Greens were not seen mating (although cubs arrived a couple of months later) perhaps because copulation took place in water. Captive otters have been observed mating in water as well as on land but most frequently in water. Mating lasts from ten to thirty minutes and may occur several times during the few days the animals are together. It may be preceded by a great deal of apparently playful behaviour with the male chasing the female into and out of the water, the two otters swimming and diving together and engaging in mock fighting. Following this short period of courtship, the two animals separate and resume their solitary habits.

No doubt some of the behaviour observed between courting otters could be described as play but if, as is often supposed, courtship behaviour is designed to give the animals a chance to ensure that both are ready for mating, it does have an extremely serious intent. Some of the activities could be interpreted as the female trying to resist the advances of the male, perhaps while she makes up her mind whether he is a suitable mate or not. The production of offspring and the survival of genes into succeeding generations is fundamentally the most important aspect of any animal's life and not to be undertaken lightly.

Play

Otters are renowned for their playful behaviour but, in the wild at least, it seems to be rather more rare than is generally supposed. Hans Kruuk and his colleagues observed few meetings between otters but of eighty-four they recorded, twenty-five per cent included 'playful behaviour' while forty-five per cent involved threats or avoidance. Play is certainly a common activity in captivity but, of course, captive otters know where the next meal is coming from and do not have to conserve their energy for important activities like foraging. In the wild, play most often involves young otters which, like many small animals, indulge in a wide range of activities with no obvious, immediate purpose but which probably help them in gaining skills for life: mock fighting, mock hunting or just improving co-ordination. One young otter studied by Hugh Watson had no brothers and sisters and tried instead to engage its mother in play, particularly wrestling in the water. The cub would also play on its own, rolling amongst the kelp fronds and biting at the stalks or juggling with small crabs.

Cubs are very playful ...

... but adults only occasionally indulge in the wild.

Two particular misconceptions about play ought to be dispelled. The first concerns sliding. 'Play sliding' (i.e. sliding with no obvious purpose) often occurs in captivity if a suitable slope is provided but there are only a few reports from the wild and mainly for the North American river otter. I have quite often found 'slides' in the UK but these are simply routes into and out of the water down steep banks. North American otters also use sliding as a means of travelling over snow. They gallop along to build up speed and then launch themselves along the ground. For a short-legged animal in snow this seems to be a fairly effective means of progression. There are good observations of these otters repeatedly running to the top of a slope and sliding down it – a behaviour which can have no real 'purpose' other than play. Sadie Stevens once saw a group of three otters slide sixteen times for an average of about four seconds per slide.

Second, there is a belief that otters will play with their prey, particularly eels, throwing them in the air and catching them repeatedly. Again, this seems to be particularly likely with captive otters, who know that if the eel escapes they will be given something else to eat instead. However, it has also been seen in the wild and it may simply be part of the otter's killing behaviour. Eels will continue to writhe for some time and the otter may simply be trying to make sure that its meal is dead before consuming it.

This does not mean that otters never play in the wild as they often do in captivity, but it is important to recognise that the popular image of otters as carefree playful animals does not reflect the reality of their natural lives.

Aggressive behaviour

There is some evidence that females may become aggressive after giving birth. In particular, one female that was studied in captivity in Sweden underwent a change in behaviour after her cubs were born. She chased and attacked the male who until that time had shared her pen for several months without any signs of aggression between them. Wild female otters in Shetland can also be aggressive to males when they have young cubs.

More serious aggression than the henpecking of males may occur from time to time. A Danish zoo kept two male otters in the same enclosure as a female with no trouble until they reached maturity. Eventually the two dogs fought with each other until one escaped over a fence but not before it had been bitten in the scrotum. Don Jefferies discovered similar injuries in a road casualty and otter hunters, who would sometimes keep the baculum (penis bone) of a male otter as a trophy, occasionally found that they had been fractured. Evidently otters in the wild also resort to attacking below the belt.

In Shetland the most common interaction seen between adult male otters was fighting. This usually occurred on land and was brief but fierce, with the animals noisily chasing one another until one fled.

In recent years evidence has been accumulating to show that, in the wild, otters frequently suffer severe wounds at the teeth of their relatives. Vic Simpson's careful observations of otters on which he carried out post-mortem examinations (mostly road traffic casualties) reveal that about forty per cent suffered from bite wounds, most of which could be attributed to other otters and about a quarter of which led to death.

Over the period 1996–2003, Vic found that the proportion steadily increased and that both males and females were affected. Wounding was concentrated on the face, feet and beneath the tail – one unfortunate male had been castrated.

Less serious aggression also occurs and may be resolved without resort to violence. Otters with large items of food will warn off attempts to come too close with a 'yickering' noise. Usually this results in a retreat, at least until the otter in possession has finished its meal, but it does not always work and adult males have been watched stealing food from smaller animals. Similar squabbles have been observed when two otters wanted to use the same den; usually one will back down rather than risk a proper fight.

Not all interactions are so unfriendly and some recent observations by Melanie Findlay challenge the assumption that female otters keep males away from the cubs for fear of cannibalism. Melanie used a camera trap outside a breeding holt and found that an adult male would regularly rest inside it even when the cubs were very small. Whether this male was the father of the cubs, a relative of the female (brother or son) or unrelated to either is unknown.

BREEDING

When do otters breed?

For a long time the answer to this question seemed to be, 'At any time of year'. There are records of otter cubs being seen in every month in England with no apparent peak of births in any one season. Liz Chadwick found no evidence of seasonal variation in the number of otters pregnant or lactating in 600 otters examined post-mortem from England and Wales between 1992 and 2003. The reason for this is probably that food is readily available throughout the year and English winters are not too severe.

In Sweden, on the other hand, where the lakes are frozen for much of the winter, there is every reason for the cubs to be born early enough to ensure that they are well grown before the severe weather returns. Hardly surprising, then, that they are born in spring.

A little further south, in northern Scotland, otters living inland seem to produce cubs throughout the year. In mild winters this is a successful strategy but when the weather is harsh a high proportion of the litters are lost if the cubs are small. Further north again, in Shetland, they are seasonal breeders, like those in Sweden, but the Shetland otters give birth in the summer. More than half the litters in Shetland are born in May and June and eighty-five per cent in the period from May to the end of August. Here, however, it is not the severity of the weather that is important but the lack of food in winter and early spring. From January to April there are far fewer fish in the inshore area than for the rest of the year and, although the fish present tend to be larger specimens, the total amount of food available is about ten times less in March and April than in July and August. Giving birth in the summer means that, while the female has the heaviest drain on her needs, during lactation, food is most abundant and readily available.

Latitude is not the only factor, however, and in Spain, Jordi Ruiz-Olmo found that eighty-five per cent of otters living close to the Pyrenees gave birth between March and June. Further south in Mediterranean rivers fifty-seven per cent of otters gave birth in winter (December to February). In both cases this could be linked to seasonal changes in food supply.

How often?

Although otters seem to be capable of having litters in consecutive years, not all of them do. In Shetland one female failed to breed in three consecutive years whereas some bred in alternate years and others had cubs every year. It is difficult to be certain whether this variation is due to differences in the quality of the females or the quality of their home ranges. Food availability certainly plays an important part since the total number of cubs reared in a year when food was abundant was four times higher than when it was scarce. On average sixty per cent of adult females bred each year.

Young otter harassing its mother.

Where otters do not have a well-defined breeding season, they have the option of having litters more than a year apart but without waiting for two full years. John Watt found that on Mull young otters stayed with their mothers a long time before becoming independent and for two females this resulted in the females having an interval of longer than a year between litters. Once again, food supply seemed to be the key factor determining this.

Gestation and birth

The gestation period of otters has been worked out by studying captive animals and the time from the last known mating to birth is close to sixty-three days, much the same as for other similarly-sized animals.

Interestingly, although several other species of otter as different in size as Asian short-clawed and giant otters have the same gestation period, the North American river otter has a gestation period of eleven months because the embryo undergoes delayed implantation. This species comes into breeding condition and mates soon after giving birth in the spring. Instead of the embryos developing normally they stop growing after a few days when they consists of little balls of cells, known as blastocysts. At this stage they would normally implant into the wall of the uterus so that they could obtain the benefit of the nutrients in the mother's blood supply. Instead they float in the uterus for several months until, two months before the cubs are due to be born, they finally implant and continue their normal development. A similar process occurs in sea otters, badgers, stoats, grey seals and roe deer as well as other species but the reasons behind it are still not fully understood.

Although cubs have occasionally been raised in quite public places (such as at a ferry terminal in Shetland) it is believed that otters normally give birth in more secure dens, well away from potential disturbance. These may be on small tributaries away from a main river but it seems unlikely that the female would be too far from good feeding areas since, the more time she spends travelling to feed, the longer the cubs must be left alone.

When Geoff Liles tried to define otter breeding sites so that they could be found and protected, he discovered that it was not easy to give clear advice. In the first place people have not always recognised that females might give birth in one place, a natal den, and bring their young up in another. This behaviour is well documented in Shetland and is suspected elsewhere. It is also important to recognise the difference between the den in which the otters live and the area surrounding it which could also be important in providing security and possibly feeding areas. Geoff was concerned to ensure that the whole area was recognised as a 'breeding site' and afforded protection, not just the den.

He described five otter breeding sites in Wales, two on lakes and three beside the banks of rivers. All had either reeds, woodland or scrub to provide cover and, for four of them, the area was between four and fifty hectares. He found that two of the natal dens were on islands, and that one was in an old badger tunnel, one under gorse and bramble thicket and one under a garage. Two other sites in England were also described and in most cases the den was in an area of good cover and not too far from good foraging grounds.

Litter size
This varies between one and five with two or three cubs the most common. Coastal otters seem to have smaller litters than those inland, the average produced in Shetland being about 1.8 compared to between 2.3 and 2.8 for various inland studies. Coastal otters in other areas also have smaller litters. The reasons for this difference are not at all clear but the fact that there is a consistent difference suggests that there may be some common factor. This could be connected with the ecology of the otters in different

habitats but it could simply be a difference in the way the data were collected. If you calculate litter sizes from seeing the family groups when they have left the breeding den you exclude any cubs which have died in the first few weeks of life. Counts of embryos in dead otters, on the other hand, will not show this early mortality. Philip Wayre's records of captive otters show that the average litter size at birth is 2.4 but the average number reared to independence is 1.8 so comparisons of litter sizes from the wild also need to take into account the age of the cubs.

GROWING UP

Philip Wayre has watched and filmed the development of otter cubs inside a specially constructed breeding den so we have a fairly comprehensive record of the growth and behaviour of captive otters during the first few weeks of life. Compared to some animals they are slow developers. At birth the cubs are tiny, about 12 cm long and weighing between 100 and 150 grams. They are blind, helpless and covered with short pale fur. At this stage they suckle every few hours and make small chirruping noises but do very little else. Their eyes do not open until they are four or five weeks old by which time they can crawl unsteadily around but not walk properly. At this age a cub will weigh 700–800 grams rising to between 1 and 1.2 kg by the time it is two months old. The first solid food is taken at about seven weeks but it is another two or three weeks before they

Cubs do not venture outside the den until about ten weeks old.

venture outside the den to play and fully three months before they first meet the medium with which they will become so familiar, water.

For animals that will eventually become so much at home in water, cubs can seem very reluctant at first. There are many stories of females encouraging or even compelling their cubs into the water but Philip Wayre has also watched cubs take to the water of their own accord the first time, simply following their mother into it. Within a few weeks the young otters will follow the female on her travels, learning how to seek out and catch prey for themselves. Initially, most of their food comes from the mother who must make trips back to the shore with prey for them. In Shetland, young otters still only catch a fifth of their prey for themselves by January and February when they are about eight months old. Interestingly the female tends to take larger prey to her cubs than she eats herself. This is a sensible strategy since she will need to make fewer trips to the shore with large fish for the cubs than with small ones. In fact, females with cubs seem to select larger fish than they do when just hunting for themselves.

The families begin to break up when the cubs are about nine months of age, although in some cases they stay with their mother until they are over a year old. Once independent, however, they have to fend for themselves, not just in obtaining enough food to survive on but also in finding a suitable place to settle down. Leaving home is not just a matter of bidding mother a fond farewell, it may also mean leaving behind an area that is very familiar, where the good feeding places, resting places and hiding places are well known. There may be social problems to be faced as well. Sub-adult otters in inland areas seem to live mainly in the sub-optimal, peripheral areas and if they do venture into the territories of established animals they may well have to spend much of their time looking out for the resident who may be inclined to see them off his or her territory. It is certainly a risky time and there is a higher mortality of otters in their second year of life than in subsequent ones.

The best information on dispersal of young otters comes from Idaho where a number of young American river otters were radio-tracked. In this area, where otters are not territorial, there was a variety of patterns of dispersal. Some litters of young otters stayed together for the first few months after they left home while others were solitary from the start. Some hardly moved from the areas in which they had been born while one young male travelled over 100 km during a month before settling down about 30 km from his birthplace. We have no comparable information for the Eurasian otter but it seems probable that movements like these take place. Certainly during the national otter surveys there are occasional isolated records of otters several tens of kilometres from the nearest established population and these could be dispersing young.

Otters become sexually mature at about two years of age although in captivity a male otter of only seventeen months successfully sired a litter. In the wild one might expect that females would not breed until they had established themselves in a suitable home range with a secure breeding den and adequate food. Young males might have to wait even longer if they need to compete with older, more experienced males, or take over a territory. Otters bred in captivity and released into the wild in East Anglia where the population was extremely low are believed to have bred at around two years of age.

Growing up on Mull

John Watt spent two years studying the development of young otters on Mull where he was able to watch them grow and gain experience at hunting for themselves. In this area, where food was less abundant than around the coast of Shetland, it was a slower process. John found that by six months of age young otters were still catching less than ten per cent of their food for themselves and it wasn't until they were a year old or more that they caught all their own food.

The first attempts to forage on their own occurred at seven to eight months of age but at twelve months they still spent nearly half their time hunting with their mother. It was not until they were fourteen months old that they became fully independent and even then they might still have been living within their mother's range. John also discovered that cubs were much less efficient at hunting than adults and, probably as a result of this, crabs (mainly shore crabs) made up about thirty per cent of their diet even though you get comparatively little meat on a crab. This proportion decreased to about fifteen per cent by the time they were independent and to only two to three per cent in adults.

HOW LONG DO OTTERS LIVE?

A frequent and, apparently, simple question but one which is very difficult to answer. Simple answers, even if factually correct tend to be misleading and answers that are not misleading require a certain amount of explanation.

A slightly different question, and one that is often at the back of people's minds, is 'How long *can* otters live?' This is simple, the answer is 'About ten years', but misleading because in the wild only a very small proportion of otters actually live this long, probably less than one per cent of those born. In Shetland one female otter had reached the grand old age of ten years, while another, from Norfolk, was nine years old when she died. However, these were only two otters out of many corpses studied. Very often people are interested in averages: 'What is the average length of life

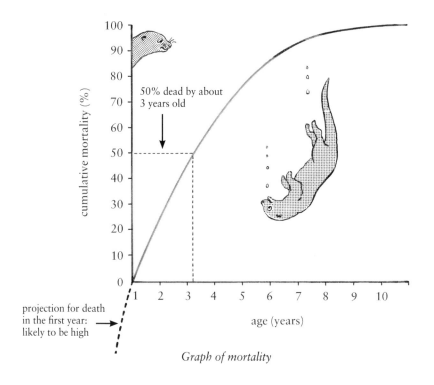

Graph of mortality

of an otter?' The answer to this, 'Probably between one and two years', is dramatically different but again obscures the true picture since many people would find it hard to envisage any animals living beyond four years if the average is less than two.

Rather than try to determine how long animals live, it is more instructive to look at when they die or, to be more precise, what proportion dies at each stage of life. Philip Wayre showed that in captivity a quarter of cubs born died before they became independent and in the wild one would not expect the figure to be lower. A study of river otters in Canada (where trapping for fur was carried out) suggested that mortality in the first year was about one third. In the same area half the surviving otters died in their second year of live so that only one third of those born reached their second birthday. Once past that age the mortality was lower with only about a quarter of the survivors dying each year.

In Shetland Hans Kruuk and his colleagues concluded that their estimate of mortality in the first year of life (twenty per cent) was too low, partly because they could not determine mortality amongst cubs which had not left the den and also because an unknown number were washed out to sea and their bodies not recovered. They found that about thirty per cent of adults died each year.

Once they get beyond a certain age the chances of survival decrease dramatically as they begin to suffer from diseases of old age. I suspect that this happens at around eight to ten years and that is why, in the wild, few if any otters live beyond their tenth birthday. In captivity, where they are cosseted, fed and attended by veterinary surgeons, otters can survive for longer, but in the real world a touch of arthritis, a few missed meals and they soon step onto the slippery slope towards starvation and death.

What do they die of?

A large number of otters die as a result of man's activities. Until about the middle of this century many were deliberately killed by trapping, shooting and hunting mainly for their fur or in the name of the preservation of fishing. More recently, otters have been protected from these threats but considerable numbers have been killed unintentionally, on the road, in fish traps and by poisoning with toxic chemicals. Otters killed on the road and in fish traps are more easily recovered than otters dying out of sight so it is impossible to know what proportion of the total mortality these figures represent. In Shetland about half the otter corpses recovered by Hans Kruuk and his colleagues had suffered a violent death, mainly on roads.

The Shetland otters that had died 'natural deaths' tended to be in poorer condition than the others and they also contained higher concentrations of toxic chemicals, especially mercury and PCBs. The significance of these compounds is discussed later but it is interesting to note that mercury occurs naturally in Shetland and in some older otters the concentration was high enough to cause poisoning. Most deaths by non-violent means occurred between March and June when fish were scarce and the fact that these animals tended to be in poor condition suggests that starvation might be an important factor. A similar pattern has emerged on rivers in northern Scotland where Kruuk and his colleagues found that over forty per cent of non-violent mortality occurred in April when food was scarcest.

Over a period of about twenty years otters found dead in England and Wales have been routinely collected and subject to post-mortem examination. Since the majority of these were road casualties, which are easily seen and frequently reported, the sample is very biased in terms of causes of death. However, the small number dying for other reasons are informative and a great deal of useful information about the health of otters has been obtained from this source.

Road deaths accounted for more than eighty per cent of deaths in southern England and just over ninety per cent elsewhere in England and Wales. In southern England a further eleven per cent died of bite wounds and subsequent infection. Other causes included young cubs which had been separated from or abandoned by their mothers and had starved or been killed by dogs. Small numbers died of infectious diseases and a few were killed illegally in snares or fyke nets.

Bite wounds were found on a large number of otters and the proportion increased over time until they were recorded in more than half the otters examined in south-west England each year. A few bites could be identified as being from dogs or mink but the majority were caused by other otters. Attacks were directed at the face, feet or genital area and were recorded in females as well as males, although the seasonal pattern differed between the sexes. Deaths occurred when the wound became infected but many otters were found with healed wounds.

Parasites and disease

Captive otters are susceptible to a bacterium rejoicing in the name of *Leptospira icterohaemorrhagiae*. This is carried by rats and causes Weil's disease in humans, an extremely unpleasant form of jaundice which sometimes leads to death (in man as well as otters). A study of seventy otter kidneys (where leptospires are usually found) revealed that three were infected, though not with the most pathogenic type. People have also worried about distemper and 'Aleutian disease', two viral diseases which occur in ranch-bred mink but, to date, neither has been found to be prevalent in wild otters.

Some otters killed on the road had lesions which might have indicated bacterial infection. Cultures of many of these did reveal the presence of bacteria, most of them of fairly common types such as Streptococcus and

Staphylococcus species. None had TB.

Several parasites have been found in the guts of otters including thorny-headed worms, roundworms and tapeworms; in one sample of otters from Shetland half were parasitised. Most of the parasites found infect various predators of fish but one species of tapeworm was specific to otters and the thorny-headed worm species mainly parasitises seals.

Recent post-mortems of otters have shown that a type of bile fluke previously unknown from Britain occurs in otters and mink, particularly in Somerset and adjacent counties. It is called *Pseudamphistomum truncate*. (Why do harmful organisms seem to get all the best names?) Its normal range is Eastern Europe. It was probably introduced with two species of fish (the top-mouth gudgeon and the sun bleak) that have been released into the wild in that area. Nearly twenty per cent of 160 otters examined from the area from 2005 to 2007 were infected and, although some were in poor condition, many were not. There is no evidence that the disease kills otters.

Otters do not seem to suffer much from external parasites although they occasionally carry ticks. Neither ticks nor fleas seem to mind a semi-aquatic existence because they are often found on mink and it may be that they would be more common on otters were it not for their dense coats.

Many parasites are very particular about the species of animal they will live on and there is one species of louse which is only found on the Eurasian otter. Its name, *Lutridia exilis*, reflects this but it is far from common and has only been recorded ten times since its first discovery in 1815 including three times in Britain (in 1919, 1930 and most recently in 1987). It is very small (about 1.2 mm long) so it could easily be missed and, as there are not many people who spend their time looking for lice on otters, the rarity of finds is perhaps not surprising. Even so, up to 150 otter corpses were carefully searched by Nature Conservancy Council scientists over a period of nearly thirty years and only one, from the remote island of Lewis, had *Lutridia exilis*.

On the other hand, I have seen one otter that was crawling with ticks although she was emaciated and in very poor condition. This particular animal was also blind, a condition which seems to be more common in otters than one might expect. James Williams, a naturalist in Somerset with a keen interest in otters, collected twenty-two records of blind otters, most of which had lost the sight of both eyes. Some of these were in poor condition, but ten were described as being in good condition so they were presumably still able to hunt. They came from a wide area in Britain although most were from the south and there were no records prior to 1957, despite attempts to find one. Since otter hunters were keen diarists and often recorded peculiarities of the animals they killed, James concluded that blindness was a new phenomenon, but was not able to explain it.

Vic Simpson's careful studies of the otters he carried out post-mortems on led to the discovery of damaged retinas in a significant number, nearly a third of sixty-two that died between 1996 and 1999. He attributed this to abnormalities in development which are linked to low levels of vitamin A that, in turn, can be caused by toxic chemical such as PCBs and many pesticides. Otters with damaged retinas did indeed have low levels of vitamin A and also the concentration of dieldrin in their livers was three times higher than those without.

Predation

There are no natural predators of otters in Britain today, as described earlier. The main 'predator' of otters, now that they are protected from persecution, is the motor car. One other 'unnatural predator' is the domestic dog and about a third of the otters that died as a result of bite wounds had been bitten by dogs. These were all cubs and immature animals but a few adult otters had bite wounds on the throat, abdomen or hind limb where they had probably been bitten by dogs though not killed by them.

ARE OTTERS PESTS?

Much of the rest of this book is concerned with the relationship between man and the otter which, until quite recently, has always been a rather one-sided affair with the otter on the losing side. First we persecuted them, then we poisoned them, now at long last we are trying to protect them. Even so, now that otters are becoming more common, they are once more being thought of as pests by some people, notably fishermen interested in trophy or expensive species in the UK and by people who farm freshwater fish commercially for food in other parts of Europe.

Originally, persecution was carried out in the name of preservation of otters' prey. In the sixteenth century they were regarded as serious pests and a bounty placed on their heads because of attacks on fish ponds and fish traps. At that time they were either trapped or hunted with hounds and in some areas there were local laws requiring fishermen to keep a dog for hunting otters. Fish were an important source of protein and competition from the otter was not to be tolerated. It is quite impossible now to judge whether otters really did reduce the food available to man but in well-stocked fish ponds they could have been a major problem. Anywhere that prey is concentrated makes for good hunting.

In the UK today fish farming for food is carried out mainly with salmon and mainly in Scotland. The fish are maintained in large netted enclosures in the sea, close to the shore and usually sheltered from the worst weather. Thousands of fish are packed into very small areas and fed on a highly nutritious diet to fatten them up for the table – in theory, a paradise for otters. Although there are some complaints about the attentions of otters, they have not reached the proportions one would expect from the proliferation of such farms. This is because, although there is a high density of otters and of fish farms in the lochs and sea lochs of western Scotland, the fish are maintained in netted enclosures from which it is reasonably easy to exclude the otters.

Fish farms in freshwater are more vulnerable as are artificially stocked fisheries. In the past, the highest value fish were trout and this, combined with the fact that many have been established for a long time, meant that owners are more likely to safeguard their fish from predation, by fish-eating birds and mink as well as otters. In recent years, however, there has been a

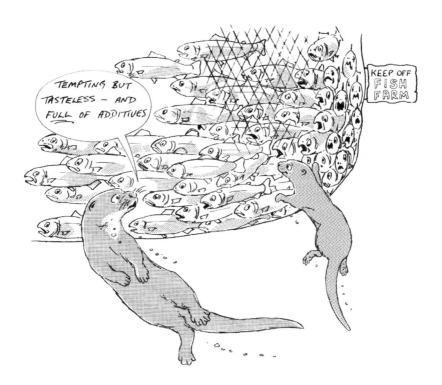

dramatic increase in the keeping of fish in ponds, lakes and gravel pits, both for coarse fishing and pleasure, the exotic and very expensive Koi carp, for example. Stocking levels can be extremely high and a premium is placed on large fish which, being caught and released many times, can live to a considerable age.

Such 'stillwater fisheries' may be set up in areas which are only now being recolonised by otters, perhaps in ignorance of the fact that this large fish-eating predator is likely to be a threat to stocks unless suitable precautions are taken. Others may have been in existence for longer but are in places where otters were formerly absent and are now returning. Predation by otters has generated considerable controversy in the angling press and there have been calls for otters to be culled.

Aware of this, the Environment Agency has produced a leaflet entitled

Otters and Stillwater Fisheries. This explains the risk and outlines measures which can be taken to reduce it, mainly through the use of fencing. These measures can be extremely expensive, however, particularly on large lakes, and, despite the high value of the fisheries, there is resistance to paying such costs.

In the end, one has to question whether it is reasonable that people who want to indulge in leisure pastimes such as these should be able to do so at the expense of our native wildlife. It is difficult to see how, under present legislation, any cull could be condoned. Without a licence it would certainly be illegal to kill otters and to obtain a licence one would need to show that there are no satisfactory alternatives and that a cull would solve the problem. Since removing one otter merely makes space for another to move in, this is not a practical solution.

Similar problems occur elsewhere. In some Eastern European countries carp farming for food has a long history and there are huge areas with large numbers of ponds which are carefully managed for fish production. Elsewhere new species are being farmed on the coast – sea bass, sea bream and sole in Portugal, for example, and otters have not been slow to realise this.

As otters return to places where they were formerly present but recently absent some conflicts inevitably occur. We do not depend on stocks of freshwater fish for food these days and in the UK the problems occur mainly with a leisure industry. However, it is an industry which affects very many people and in which some people have invested considerable sums of money. In general it is far better to deal with the conflicts at the stage where developments are planned rather than retrospectively and one can only hope that, with time, it will become easier to reconcile the needs of conservation with those of the anglers.

HUNTING OTTERS

Otters have been hunted by man since time immemorial, initially just for their fur, later to protect fish stocks and more recently for pleasure. Even hunting with hounds goes back at least eight hundred years. There was a King's Otterhunt in 1175 when Henry II was monarch and the regal interest continued through the reigns of King John, who was very fond of his otterhounds apparently; Edward II, who had a pack but spent more of his time hunting deer; Henry IV, who maintained a 'valet of our otterhounds'; and Henry VIII who also kept a pack of otterhounds. It seems pretty clear that for much of this time the main motive for otter hunting was pleasure but, although it was sometimes quite fashionable, it was generally seen as a lesser sport than hunting 'noble' quarry such as deer or even foxes. It was not confined to Britain and in the 1930s a pack based in central France (Monsieur Guyot's Otterhounds) and two in the Irish Republic (Cork City Otterhounds and Fermoy Otterhounds) reported their results in *The Year Book of Otterhunting* produced in England. Nevertheless, hunting otters with dogs for sport has always been a mainly British pastime.

There is a great deal of hunting literature and a surprising number of books devoted to the histories of individual otterhunts. Even today, more than thirty years after hunting ceased in Britain, people still collect these books and new ones have recently been published either as anthologies of earlier writings or as facsimiles or reprints of books long out of date. They make interesting reading. Otter hunters had a great respect for the otter and in some of the older books long chases are recorded with great relish. There is often a strong feeling of respect for otters which provided a good chase. In a book about the history of the Dartmoor Otterhounds one otter which eluded the hounds for nearly two and a half hours before being finally killed was described as 'the hero of the day'. An otter which had provided such a good chase might be allowed to go free, presumably in the hope that it would provide another good day's sport on a later hunt. Conversely otters which succumbed rapidly were often regarded as rather feeble creatures. At the same time, while many people enjoyed the thrill of the chase, not all looked forward to the kill and many people went hunting because it was the only way they could be sure of seeing otters.

During a hunt the hounds would first 'draw' the river, searching for the scent or 'drag' of the otter. Once found this had to be traced to where

Otterhound

the animal was lying up, a feat requiring some skill on the part of the huntsman to ensure that the hounds followed the trail towards it rather than away. When the otter was located, either seen escaping or tracked to a den or burrow, it was recorded as a 'find'. If it did not try to escape, perhaps because it was in a secure den, attempts would be made to bolt it using terriers, poles or even spades. The hounds were held back until the otter had a chance to get away ('given law') and were then allowed to set off in pursuit. Hunt followers would play a part by keeping a look out for the otter and sometimes by helping to form a barrier in the shallows when they would line up across the stream waving their sticks in the water to turn it back towards the hounds (a 'stickle'). The hunt might last a few minutes or a few hours and about half the otters found were killed while the rest escaped, or were allowed to escape.

The otterhound

When otters were still reasonably numerous throughout Britain there were over a dozen packs of hounds maintained specifically for hunting them. Many of these packs had a mixture of breeds with English and Welsh foxhounds predominating, but two packs, the Dumfriesshire and the Kendal and District Otterhounds, had packs of purebred hounds with pedigrees stretching back into the nineteenth century. It is clear that hunts commonly carried out judicious cross-breeding to improve the strain in their packs so it is not surprising to find the origin of the otterhound itself in a cross – between a bloodhound and rough-coated French hound (the Griffon Vendéen). The result is best described as looking like a long-haired bloodhound and it was particularly noted for its stamina, its voice and its very keen nose, all pre-requisites for a successful otter-hunting hound.

The total population of pure otterhounds was never very high because only two hunts had purebred packs while others had a few otterhounds together in their mixed-breed packs. When the otter population declined to the level at which legal protection became inevitable and otter hunting ceased, there was some risk that the extinction of the otterhound was imminent. However, some of the packs were kept on for hunting mink (and still do so today, thirty years later), while the masters of the Dumfries and the Kendal and District Otterhounds decided that in order to maintain the breed it should be registered with the Kennel Club and bred for show rather than for hunting.

Sixty-six dogs were registered and a Kennel Club breed standard can now be found on its website together with the names of three breeders. There are also three websites dedicated to the breed which seems now to be assured of survival.

As each pack consisted of twenty to thirty hounds, one might expect that the otter would have little or no chance of escape from such formidable 'predators' but, although dogs can travel much faster on land, they cannot swim as fast as otters, nor can they dive. On the other hand, they can run along the bank to keep up with the otter and stickles were formed by hunt followers to turn the otter back towards the hounds. Once the otter was amongst the hounds its chances of escape were much lower, especially as, if it did slip away, people on the bank would be looking out for it. Some otters got away through their own devices while others were allowed to escape by the huntsman. Hounds on their own (even in a pack) would probably not be able to catch many otters but with human help they could kill up to three-quarters of those found, though half was more usual.

Incidentally, there seems to be no formal guidance on whether 'otterhound' and 'otterhunt' should be one word or two. Spell checkers and dictionaries seem to prefer two words but *The Yearbook of Otterhunting* was published by the Masters of 'Otterhounds' Association.

James Williams suggested to me that I should use one word for purebred 'otterhounds' but recognise that other types of dog (including foxhounds) were used to hunt otters – when they became 'otter hounds' (two words). The organisations which maintained these packs and organised 'otter hunts' (two words) were called 'Otterhunts'. I hope that is clear!

If this sounds a bit tough on the otters, just bear in mind that until the mid to late nineteenth century nets were used to ensnare them and barbed spears to impale them; methods which were considered quite barbaric by twentieth-century otter hunters. Indeed in the later stages of otter hunting, when otters became very scarce and the object became to find rather than to kill them, the stickle too was abandoned.

Like many sportsmen the hunters claimed that they were able to control the numbers of otters and prevent them reducing fish populations. However, they also maintained, particularly in the last few years of hunting, that they were keen to preserve otters. This is not really a paradox but I suspect that there is more truth in the conservation role, at least in the nineteenth century, than in the argument about controlling numbers. I have a strong suspicion that one of the reasons the otter did not suffer the fate of polecats, pine marten and wild cats in the last century was because, like foxes, they were beasts of the chase. Landowners and river keepers could be persuaded to leave the 'control' of otters to the hunt rather than taking it into their own hands. The fact that hunting was less effective than shooting and trapping and that the hunts had a vested interest in making sure that there were otters left to hunt next year was conveniently overlooked, or at least accepted in return either for compensation for damage or the opportunity to take part in hunting. Incidentally, it is very interesting to find that the mink hunts, most of which have been formed since otter hunting ceased, stress the 'control' argument while the otterhunts towards the end stressed the 'preservation' argument. Nevertheless, despite their stated aim of preserving their quarry during the second half of the twentieth century, otterhunts were quite powerless to prevent the population from declining in the face of modern threats to its well-being even though they changed from trying to kill otters to trying to count them.

One effect of the decline in otters was a reduction in the numbers of hunts and also the frequency of hunting. In 1951 there were twelve active hunts which between them hunted for 571 days finding 395 otters. In 1961 eleven hunts achieved 584 days hunting and found 314 otters. However, by 1971 the same number of hunts was only out on 371 days finding 181 otters and by 1976 there were only nine hunts which found 86 otters in 215 days. The last year in which otter hunting took place in England and Wales was in 1977 because the following year the otter was protected under the Conservation of Wild Creatures and Wild Plants Act. Several of the old otterhunts turned to hunting mink, some disbanded and one concentrated on ensuring the survival of the Otterhound as a breed.

In 2010, *Baily's Hunting Directory* listed eighteen mink hunts scattered across England and Wales of which five retained names used by packs of Otterhounds in the past. There are also two packs in Ireland, the Cork City Mink Hunt and Bride View Mink Hunt, also retaining traditional names.

Otters have also been hunted for their fur and, in many European countries where the fur trade is well established, most otter hunting has been for this purpose, using traps and to a lesser extent guns. The luxuriant fur has long been popular and otters have probably suffered for this ever since man first learnt to sew skins together. In the fifteenth century, their pelts were used as a form of currency – John, son of Dermod, had to stump up 164 otter skins in lieu of rent owed to Henry IV and as early as the fourteenth century there are records of otter skins being imported to Britain from the continent. Even in the 1960s and 1970s otters were being trapped for their skins in parts of Scotland, at that time they were worth about £10–£15 each.

In other European countries substantial numbers were being killed, about a thousand per year in Sweden during the 1940s and 1950s and two hundred per year in Denmark. Even during the 1970s, six hundred were being killed each year in Norway. The greatest numbers, however, came from Russia where between four and eight thousand were killed annually from 1940 to 1970, although in the early 1970s the numbers were considerably lower and hunting was banned in at least one region.

Despite these culls, it seems unlikely that killing otters for their fur or for sport has been responsible for the declines that have taken place in most European countries. Toxic chemicals are much more likely culprits. This is not the case for other species of otter, however. The sea otter nearly became extinct in the second half of the nineteenth century, mainly because its habits made it much easier to find and kill. The giant otter has suffered a similar fate in some parts of its range during the twentieth century and its habits may also make it more vulnerable to hunters. Giant otters are more sociable than Eurasian otters, living in large (and sometimes quite noisy) family groups which are active by day, and are also quite inquisitive. It's also possible that the indigenous people of South America are more effective hunters than those in Europe.

DECLINE AND FALL

It was in August 1962 that an article, written by Jack Ivester Lloyd, appeared in the magazine *Gamekeeper and Countryside*. It was entitled 'Where are the Otters?' and the author, a keen hunter himself, explained that the otterhunts had found very few otters over the past few seasons. He speculated on the reasons for this and concluded that over-zealous river clearance was at least partly to blame, in particular the removal of bankside trees, osier clumps and reedbeds, perhaps combined with excessive water extraction leading to lower water levels. Another hunter suggested that too much disturbance by fishermen, picnickers and bathers had driven the otters away.

This lack of otters clearly worried the hunts and from that time on there was a policy of reducing the number killed during hunting. Before 1960 about half the otters that were 'found' by hounds were killed but that proportion declined steadily during the 1960s till by 1970 it was less than fifteen per cent and did not exceed that level while hunting continued. By the 1970s the policy was to kill only those thought to be injured or diseased or if strongly urged to do so by a landowner suffering damage. If you bear in mind that fewer otters were being found at that time anyway, it is not too surprising to find that the average kill in the 1970s was only eleven per year over the whole country.

The scientific community also became concerned but was not able to produce tangible results so quickly. It was not until 1969 that the report of a sub-committee of The Mammal Society was published, which confirmed fears that numbers of otters had declined seriously, especially in the south. The authors of this report found it very difficult to obtain firm evidence of a decline from the 160 individuals and twenty river authorities which responded to requests for information. Although many people believed that there had been a decline they could not provide data to back this up. In contrast, the otterhunts were able to pass on records of the numbers of days they had been out hunting and the numbers of otters they had found and killed.

As the hunts did not all spend the same amount of time hunting each year, the figures were converted to a proportion which indicated the number of otters found per hundred days hunting so that they could be compared. There was quite a lot of variation between different hunts and different years but in the years 1900, 1937, 1947 and 1957 the average success rate was between sixty-four and eighty otters per hundred days hunting. However, in 1967 the average was forty-four otters per hundred days with all the hunts but one showing a decline since 1957. The authors concluded that the decline had taken place, or at least started, between 1957 and 1967, but could not pinpoint the date more accurately. It was nearly ten more years before we could get any closer to the exact timing and causes of the decline.

The report suggested six factors which might have caused the decline: the severe winter of 1962/63, pesticides, increase in fishing, increases in tourism and pleasure boating, trapping for fur, and destruction of habitat, but could not determine which, if any, was the most important. In 1977, the report of the 'Joint Otter Group' added to these a further five pressures on the otter which had also been suggested as causes of the decline: hunting, disease, road casualties, the spread of mink, and protection of fisheries. Again, it was not possible to determine the significance of any of these.

During 1977 I moved to Cornwall and met a keen hunter who showed me copies of *The Yearbook of Otterhunting* dating back to 1950. Although he did not have a complete set, another acquaintance from Northumberland also had an incomplete set and between the two I was able to piece together the records for all the otterhunts from 1950 to 1966. The Mammal Society's first report had figures for 1967 and a second one published five years later took the records up to 1971. Using these data it was possible to pinpoint the start of the decline much more closely and, with the help of Don Jefferies of the Nature Conservancy Council, I could show that it must have started round 1957 in much of southern Britain. This date, together with the fact that the decline was more or less simultaneous over a wide area but most serious in the south, enabled us to reject many of the suggested causes of the decline and we came to the conclusion that the introduction of a new kind of insecticide (dieldrin and related compounds) was responsible. Many birds and mammals were killed by these chemicals when they were first used and there were dramatic declines in the populations of some birds of prey such as peregrine falcons and sparrowhawks.

Dieldrin and related compounds such as aldrin, and heptachlor were first used in 1955 for a variety of purposes. A particularly important one was as seed dressing for cereals but they were also used for sheep dipping, in the woollen industry, for moth-proofing carpets and blankets, and for timber treatment. They are extremely effective pesticides but are very persistent and continue to act for a long time. Unfortunately, they are poisonous to birds and mammals as well as to insects.

Some animals were poisoned directly, mainly by feeding on dressed seeds. Huge numbers of finches and small songbirds died, as well as many woodpigeons, although fewer tears were shed over these. Other animals, the carnivorous species, received their poison second-hand by feeding on the seed-eaters. Many peregrine falcons, barn owls, sparrowhawks and foxes were killed in this way. The insecticides soon found their way into the rivers, leaching through the soil as run-off from fields or as waste from sheep dip in others. Once there they were absorbed by tiny micro-organisms in the water and the concentrations built up to a higher level in the fish which fed on them. From there it is a short step to the fish-eating birds, such as herons and grebes, and mammals, like the otter, and with each step in the food chain, the concentration of chemicals in the body increased.

In the end the predators may die of poisoning. Although there are no records of otters being found dead of pesticide poisoning during the 1950s and 60s (the first case was recorded in 1972) both foxes and badgers were found dead and dying from this secondary poisoning as were many birds of prey. The lack of dead otters is no surprise when you consider how scarce they are compared to foxes and badgers which also live and forage in areas where their bodies are far more likely to be spotted. Unfortunately, even if otters were not killed outright, the population could still have suffered from the effects of sublethal poisoning. Once the pollutants reach a critical level they begin to affect the physiology of the animals. In particular, the reproductive system can be affected resulting in a variety of problems, from unusual behaviour, such as egg smashing in birds, to sterility. Significantly there were reports of fewer badger and otter cubs being seen during the late 1950s and early 1960s. Indeed, this was even mentioned in Jack Ivester Lloyd's original article.

From 1962 onwards there were a series of bans on the use of dieldrin and similar compounds; first for spring sown cereal, then for various other seed dressings, for sheep dip in 1966 and for autumn and winter sown cereals in 1975. By the late 1970s few agricultural uses remained and the large numbers of birds and animals killed by these chemicals were a thing of the past. Peregrine falcon and sparrowhawk populations recovered in numbers but the recovery of the otter population was slower and in some areas it continued to decline into the 1980s. The reasons for this are not entirely clear and probably vary from place to place. However, post-mortem studies on otters killed on the roads during the 1990s showed that some of these chemicals were still exerting an effect.

Vic Simpson's careful examinations of otters killed on the road during the 1990s revealed a number of abnormalities, including low levels of vitamin A, defects to the retina and abnormally large thyroid glands, all of which could be linked to high levels of toxic chemicals. He was also able to show that the levels of some chemicals and abnormalities decreased over time.

Over the past twenty years otters have increasingly returned to their old haunts in Britain and this pattern of recovery is described later. First we shall take a brief aside to look at the relationship between mink and otters and at the ways in which otter populations are assessed now that otter hunting has ceased.

OTTERS AND MINK

It must be a hard life being a mink. Just about everyone seems to hate them. I have been fascinated by them for many years but I despair of persuading more than a few fellow admirers that this charming little creature is a welcome addition to Britain's mammalian fauna. 'Vicious killers', 'bloodthirsty brutes', 'savage invaders'; the epithets rain down on this attractive furry animal rather smaller than the average cat. Mink first arrived in Britain in the late 1920s brought by fur farmers who bred them for their luxuriant fur. Small numbers probably escaped from the start but it was not until the mid to late 1950s that they started breeding in the wild and brought down the wrath of the British public on their heads, just because they killed some poultry and a few fish.

I am not going to defend the mink at great length here (they are after all, an alien invasive species) but I do want to consider one accusation, that it was in some way responsible for the decline of the otter. The reasons for this allegation are quite straightforward, that over much of Britain,

Feral mink

and at several localities in particular, there was a remarkably short period of time between the arrival of mink and the disappearance of otters. The fact that in other places the otter disappeared before mink arrived tends to go unnoticed, not least because otters tend not to leave a sign saying 'gone away' when they become extinct. Also overlooked was the fact that in some areas (Devon and Cornwall for example) the two species have co-existed since the mink first began to spread.

Taking Britain as a whole, the start of the decline of the otter was in the mid to late 1950s, exactly the same as the start of the spread of mink. This was an extraordinary piece of bad timing on the part of the mink which should have had the good sense to wait for another ten years or so before starting to conquer Britain. Even so, the otter's decline occurred simultaneously over much of the country, but at the time mink were confined to a few rivers in just three or four counties. Further evidence against the linking of the mink's spread with the otter's demise is provided by recent surveys which show that in two of the areas where mink have been established longest (south-west Wales and south-west England) the otter populations are doing best.

Although the evidence for mink driving out otters is very weak, it is worth looking in a bit more detail at the ways in which mink are supposed to have driven otters out. The least likely one I have heard is that otters do not like the smell of mink. I can well understand this, having occasionally felt the full force of the mink's scent glands which it occasionally discharges when upset by being caught in a trap. However, mink do not smell any better or worse than other carnivores such as badgers, foxes, weasels, or even otters, except when they are frightened. The smelliest British carnivore is probably the polecat (it used to be known as the 'foumart', short for foul marten) and otters have been sharing their ranges with polecats in the UK for thousands of years without trouble so I find it hard to believe that a few smelly mink would displace them.

Apart from this there seem to be four main accusations: (1) that mink compete with otters for food; (2) that they aggressively drive otters out; (3) that they carry diseases which could spread to otters; (4) that they kill otter cubs.

Competition for food is in many ways the most interesting and, superficially at least, the most likely. The diet of mink is very similar to that

The mink's secret weapon?

of otters in the range of prey although there are considerable differences in emphasis. While otters concentrate on food caught in water, mink are much more likely to take prey from beside water or even on land. Over a wide range of habitats the proportion of fish to birds to mammals in the mink's diet is approximately equal, with frogs forming an important item in a few areas. Mink are the jacks of all trades among British carnivores, their diet overlapping to some extent with many of the native species but, like proverbial jacks of all trades, they are masters of none. Otters are better at catching fish, polecats better at rabbiting and hunting birds, and stoats and weasels are superior ratters, mousers and hunters of voles.

As far as the otter is concerned, competition could occur for fish, which form from twenty to fifty-five per cent of the mink's diet and sixty to ninety per cent of the otter's. However, otters are much better at catching fish than mink and should have little difficulty in out-competing them. It is important to bear in mind that competition occurs when something is in short supply; if there is plenty to go round there is no problem. In Sweden, when otters are confined to fishing on streams in the winter because the lakes are frozen, it is the mink which moves away to the smaller, less productive areas, not the otters.

Such 'scramble' competition is only one form of interaction between two species with similar diets. Another is known as 'interference'. In this case, one species, usually the larger, makes sure it does not have to share the food supply by using threats or physical violence. Could mink, which rarely weigh more than 1.5 kg, really drive out otters when even the females (which are smaller than males) weigh 5 kg or more? I doubt it, especially when you bear in mind the fact that otters occasionally eat mink. The much-quoted viciousness of mink is no greater than you would expect from a carnivore of this size. Predators need to be fierce to kill their prey which may be as large as, or even larger than, themselves. Stoats and weasels have even more ferocity per gram than mink, and otters are capable of inflicting much more serious damage because of their larger size.

The possibility of mink carrying a disease which might spread to the otter population cannot be lightly dismissed. In particular, canine distemper has often been mentioned, not least because it occurred in mink on fur farms. More recently, a dead otter from Norfolk had symptoms similar to those of Aleutian disease, another virus which affected ranched mink. Apart from these, rather tenuous, connections there is no evidence that otters in Britain have suffered from the outbreak of an infectious disease. Given the number of otter corpses that have been examined over the past thirty years, it seems likely that, if there was a problem, it would have been noticed.

The story of mink killing otter cubs is an old one but it is difficult to find a reliable first-hand account. I have heard a number of stories of small brown bodies being carried by mink and in most cases these could as easily be rats or water voles as otter cubs. Libby Lenton was sent a report by a reliable witness of a mink carrying a partly-eaten otter cub. The observer found another dead cub in a hollow tree nearby. Although the mink was not seen killing the cubs this is the nearest we have to evidence that it happens. Even so, mink are much smaller than adult otters which might be expected to guard their young fiercely and I feel that it is most unlikely that this is a serious problem.

There was a suggestion at one time that, even if mink were not responsible for the original decline of the otter, perhaps their presence would stop it from recovering again. Happily, there is now good evidence throughout Britain to show that this is not so, despite the fact that we have had mink breeding wild for over fifty years the otter population continues to recover. On balance, there is little doubt that the creature that has had the greatest effect on otter populations is man and there is little to be gained by trying to transfer some of the blame to the mink.

Conversely there is evidence that, as otters have returned to their former haunts, the mink has become harder to find in them. A good example is the river Teign where I studied mink for my PhD. In the 1970s I found mink scats twice as often as otter spraints but in the late 1990s, when Laura Bonesi from Oxford University carried out a follow-up study, she found otter spraints five times more abundant than mink. Laura's success at mink trapping was less than mine as well with a halving of the number of mink caught per hundred nights' trapping.

Something similar seems to have happened throughout England where the second national otter survey revealed that it was becoming more difficult to find signs of mink where otters had increased. Smaller scale studies in north-east England and the Thames catchment showed the same pattern.

Laura Bonesi explored this interaction in various ways, including following the impact of the spread of otters in the Upper Thames catchment after seventeen otters were released by the Otter Trust in 1999. Laura found that in the area where the otters were released the proportion of sample sites with signs of mink declined from seventy-seven per cent to twenty-three per cent in a year. In other parts of the catchment not then occupied by otters the proportion of sites with signs of mink remained the same.

Laura attributed this to competition between the species and suggested that mink were avoiding otters, possibly by spending more time in terrestrial habitats and less at the waterside. Support for this came from further observations which showed that mink and otters could co-exist for longer where there was an abundance of habitats harbouring terrestrial prey.

A subsequent study in the same area by Lauren Hartington revealed that, when otters were present, mink became less active at night and more active during the day. They were also lighter in weight in the presence of otters, though the average length remained the same suggesting that they were in poorer condition.

Meanwhile, in north-east England, Robbie McDonald and his colleagues carried out annual surveys of 195 sites from 1991 to 2002. At the start otters were found at eighteen per cent of the sites and mink at eighty per cent. By the end the situation had reversed with otters at eighty per cent and mink at twenty per cent; clear evidence that, as the otters returned, the mink declined.

All this sounds like good news, especially for water voles, a significant prey of mink whose numbers are declining nationally. However, unless there are substantial improvements in riparian habits for water voles (ideally wide bands of luxuriant herbaceous vegetation), it is likely that eradication, or at least local control, of mink will be needed before the voles can thrive again.

OTTER SURVEYS

When otter hunting in England and Wales came to an end in 1977 the statistical records of hunting effort and finds ceased as well. This was not as serious a problem as it might have been for two reasons. First, by that time each hunt was, on average, only active for twenty-four days per season and the average numbers of otters found per hunt per season was nine. This meant that comparisons between hunts or years were very difficult to make because the sizes of the samples were so small. Large apparent changes from one season to the next could be due to chance rather than to changes in the population. It was also apparent that some hunts increasingly concentrated their efforts on rivers where they had a good chance of finding otters and hunted less where they knew they were absent, thereby inevitably biasing the results.

Second, in 1977, the first national otter surveys of Wales, England and Scotland started, followed in 1980 by the Irish survey. Prior to that time there had been a number of smaller scale surveys carried out by volunteers. These included whole counties such as Norfolk and Suffolk, river systems such as the Tweed and various others in different parts of Britain. All gave valuable information but because of the patchy nature of observations it was difficult to build up a picture of the situation in Britain as a whole. Comparisons were difficult because people used different methods of surveying and had different levels of experience. The national surveys overcame these problems by employing and training full time surveyors who searched in a fixed pattern, putting the same amount of effort into each area and river system.

The technique involved selecting a series of sites along each river between five and eight kilometres apart. At each site 600 metres of bank was searched for signs of otters and a sheet was filled in, recording the type of river and whether or not signs were found. In Scotland and Wales the whole country was searched in this way but, in England and Ireland, the country was divided up into fifty-kilometre squares using the national grid, and alternate ones were searched. During these four surveys nearly 11,000 sites were fully surveyed and signs of otters were found at fifty-four per cent of them. However, there were some major differences between the four countries and

By the late 1970s, otters in England were largely confined to well-wooded rivers and streams in north and west Devon.

also within each country.

The greatest contrast was between England and Ireland with otters being restricted to very few parts of England (signs found at six per cent of sites) while being found more or less everywhere in Ireland (ninety-two per cent of sites). In Scotland otters were widespread (seventy-three per cent of sites) but fewer signs were found in the south particularly between the Firth of Tay, the Southern Uplands and the Firth of Clyde. This is the most populated area of Scotland and is also heavily cultivated. In Wales, signs were most common in the south-west and on the Severn catchment but were much scarcer in the south and east, with none in the Glamorgan area or Gwent, apart from a solitary spraint near Cardiff.

In England, apart from the south-west and the Welsh borders, signs were very hard to find indeed. There were small concentrations in Northumberland and North Norfolk but elsewhere they were scarce or absent.

These studies have been repeated since with very encouraging results (see table). England, Wales and Scotland were resurveyed twice, at intervals of seven years, in 1984–6 and 1991–3 with the fourth and fifth surveys carried out at intervals of approximately nine years in England and Wales. Scotland has only been surveyed once since the 1990s, in 2003–4. Ireland is more complicated since, although the first survey was carried out over the whole island, subsequent surveys have been done separately in the north and south and in both cases more sites were searched than in the first survey.

Comparisons are easiest in England and Wales where the same areas

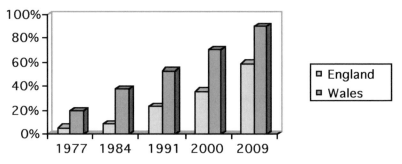

Proportion of surveyed sites where signs of otters were found.

have been surveyed each time and a dramatic recovery is revealed:

By the time of the fifth survey in England, the proportion of sites where otters were found was fifty-nine per cent overall with only the Trent (thirty-nine per cent) and Southern (nine per cent) areas having otters at less than half of the sites surveyed. Otters were found at eighty per cent or more of the sites surveyed in the south-west, Northumbria and the Wye catchment with the remainder being in between.

The most spectacular increase between the fourth and fifth surveys was on the Thames, up from eight per cent to fifty-three per cent, while the least spectacular result was from the south-east, Sussex and Kent where otters were still only present at twenty-three sites out of 244 surveyed.

In Wales, during the fifth survey, otters were found at ninety per cent of the sites surveyed, with results exceeding eighty-eight per cent in eleven out of fifteen hydrometric areas. The lowest values were in Anglesey and Mid Glamorgan where otters had only been found at eighteen per cent of sites in the fourth survey. However, nine years on, the proportion of positive sites was sixty-eight per cent and seventy per cent – a tribute perhaps to the otters breeding performance in those areas.

In Scotland, otters were widespread in some areas from the very first, so subsequent surveys concentrated more effort on those places where the recovery took place. Thus the 'Highlands and Islands' had otters at more than ninety per cent of the sites checked from the 1970s. However, the percentage of positive sites in two areas (Strathclyde and Ayrshire, Forth and the Borders) which was close to twenty per cent in the 1970s had increased to over eighty per cent by the 2000s.

In Ireland the situation is complicated by the fact that the first survey covered both the north and the south, but only half of the area was searched. Subsequent surveys dealt with the two countries separately but did cover the whole area of each. Otters are widespread in Ireland and do not appear to have undergone the severe declines which happened in England, Wales and southern Scotland. However, there was a small decline in the proportion of sites where signs were found between the first survey and in the 1980 and the early 2000s.

Overall, then, a very encouraging picture, but it has taken thirty years to get this far and, according to some calculations, it could be more than another thirty years before the otter population in England is as widely

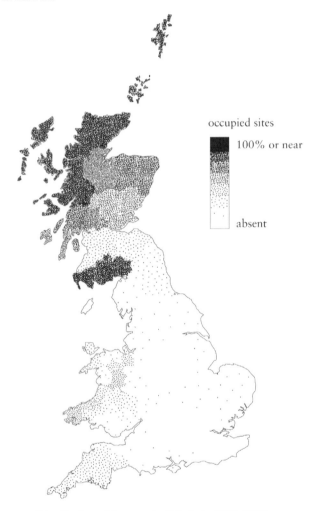

occupied sites

100% or near

absent

Distribution of the otter in Britain in 1977–1979.

distributed as it was in the early 1950s, before the decline started. Some people think that this is taking a very long time, perhaps because the habitat is less suitable or because the recovery is hindered by the numbers of otters killed on the roads. Either of these may be true but it is also worth bearing in mind that, unlike the rabbit, the otter is a slow breeder and it is bound to take a long time for the numbers to build up again.

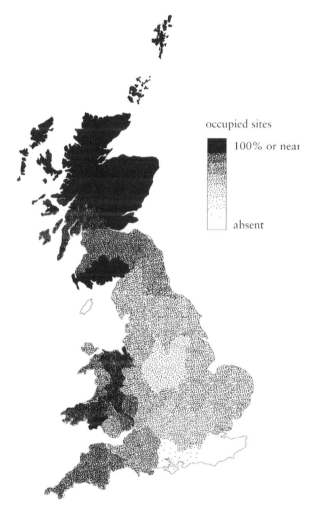

occupied sites

100% or near

absent

Distribution of the otter in Britain in 2009–2010.

Similar otter surveys have been used elsewhere in the world, though particularly in Europe where the technique pioneered in the UK has become a standard. The greatest value of these surveys is in making comparisons, either between different areas or different times, and this works well if the recommended protocols are adhered to. Nevertheless, it is extremely important to take care in interpreting the results and a certain amount of controversy has been generated. It would be very nice if there was a direct relationship between the results of surveys and numbers of otters, a doubling in the percentage of sites with signs representing a doubling of the otter population. There is some evidence of a relationship, but we do not know how to estimate numbers from survey results.

It is even more difficult when you compare different areas; some places have more suitable sprainting sites than others and not every 600-metre stretch of every river with otters will have signs within it. Even so, if you search about a hundred sites in an area 50 km square (as was done in the English survey), and find no signs of otters in any of them, it is reasonable to reach the conclusion that otters are very scarce or absent there. While in an area in which ninety per cent or more of the sites have signs, it would be reasonable to conclude that otters were widespread, although it would not necessarily mean that the numbers there were as high as they could be.

A further difficulty has occurred where people have tried to use spraint density within sites as an indicator of the size or 'health' of the otter population. It is certainly true that, where otters are known to be common, spraint is much more abundant than in areas where they are known to be present but very scarce. However, even in one area the density of spraint varies through the year so comparisons made between areas searched at different seasons would be meaningless. In Shetland, where the density of otters is well known, it was impossible to find any relationship between the density of otters and the density of spraint. Whether the situation is the same in fresh water has yet to be discovered.

Shetland is the only place where it has been possible to estimate reliably the actual population of otters. Here, otters only use a few dens each and, in an intensively studied area, Hans Kruuk and his colleagues found a close relationship between the number of well-used dens and the number of adult female otters (three dens per female). They also knew that adult females formed fifty-five per cent of the otters in the area. Following a den survey over a much wider area they were able to calculate that there were between 700 and 900 adult otters in the whole of Shetland. This survey has also been repeated though the results are very different from those of the mainland. Since the turn of the twenty-first century there has been a dramatic decline in otter numbers in Shetland, probably associated with a decline in their prey of small inshore fish.

CONSERVATION

Given the dramatic decline in the otter population – nearly to extinction in England, it is hardly surprising that a great deal of thought and effort has gone into otter conservation over the past thirty years or so. This has involved a wide range of activities: campaigning and lobbying Parliament to give otters legal protection; designating areas as 'otter havens'; planting trees and scrub beside watercourses; making artificial dens sites out of timber, concrete and even plastic; scraping up the remains of dead otters from the roads. It is likely that some of these activities were misplaced but at the time, and particularly in the 1970s and 80s, we were doing the best we could with rather limited information on otter ecology.

Legal protection

Things really began to happen in 1976 when the Friends of the Earth Otter Campaign was initiated by Angela King, Angela Potter and John Ottoway. At about the same time, the Society for the Promotion of Nature Conservation (now the Royal Society for Wildlife Trusts) joined with the Nature Conservancy Council and other bodies to form the Joint Otter Group (affectionately known as 'JOG'). One of the main aims of the FoE campaign was to get the otter protected by law (under the Conservation of Wild Creatures and Wild Plants Act). JOG's task was to find out what was known about the status of otters, establish what other information was needed, and to consider what measures should be taken (if necessary) to conserve otters. Legal protection for the otter was debated in Parliament during 1977 and approved by a small majority so that by January 1978 the otter was protected in England and Wales.

What was the otter protected from? Well, mainly from people catching it and killing it (or even attempting to catch or kill it). This had the effect that otter hunting in England and Wales ceased since, although the hunts were not trying to kill otters at that time, there was a risk that an otter might be killed accidentally or that hunting might be interpreted as an attempt to catch one. Also, I suspect the hunts realised that chasing a protected animal was a bad policy even though, at the time, they believed that the extent of the decline had been overstated. JOG did not conclude that hunting or killing otters was the reason for their low numbers so some people questioned whether legal protection was necessary or desirable. 'Why protect an animal from something that did not appear to threaten it?' My own view is that it was desirable. Not so much for what it prevented but because it made it quite clear that the otter was an endangered species and in need of special protection. This had a powerful educational effect when it came to persuading other people to do things for the benefit of the otter – a 'protected species'.

When a few years later the Wildlife and Countryside Act came into force, protection for the otter was strengthened. Otters are now protected in Scotland and Northern Ireland as well as in England and Wales and the new act makes it an offence to disturb or destroy their dens; a powerful weapon in the protection of the otter's habitat as well as the species itself.

Further legal protection for otters came in 1992 with European Community legislation, the *Council Directive 92/43/EEC on the Conservation of natural habitats and of wild fauna and flora*, fondly known as 'The Habitats Directive'. This extensive and wide ranging directive was transposed into UK legislation in 1994 and has had a significant impact on our dealings with otters (and many other species) in a number of ways.

First, it creates an obligation for the British Government to take actions to conserve otters, including the designation of a network of protected areas in which they are found. These 'Special Areas of Conservation' have to be monitored and steps taken to maintain their quality and integrity.

Second, actions (normally development) which might have detrimental effects on otters are prohibited unless steps are taken to compensate for and mitigate the effects of the actions. This has led to a situation where, before any development takes place (including road building, laying of gas pipes, water mains and so on), it is necessary to carry out an appraisal to determine whether or not it will have any impact on otters, including damaging or destroying their resting sites. Such Environmental Impact Assessments are carried out by ecologists and, if there is going to be an impact, it is necessary to apply for a licence from the appropriate Statutory Nature Conservation Organisation (Natural England, Countryside Council for Wales, Scottish Natural Heritage or the Northern Ireland Environment Agency). In order to get a licence it is necessary to demonstrate that there is a very good reason for carrying out the work, there is no reasonable alternative, adequate steps have been taken to compensate for or mitigate the impact and the conservation status of the animal will be maintained in the long term.

These obligations on developers have led to the establishment of a substantial industry of ecological consultants who advise developers on how to carry out their activities within the law and ensure that the requirements of otters and other protected species are adequately catered for. Most consultants belong to the Institute of Ecology and Environmental Management which endeavours to maintain a high standard of work and provides information and courses to train and update its members.

Habitat protection
Early efforts at practical conservation consisted of the systematic designation of Otter Havens. These were first proposed in 1975 when the Nature Conservancy Council and the Anglian Water Authority convened a small group to advise on otter conservation in East Anglia. Havens were originally envisaged as relatively small areas along rivers where the otter's needs would be particularly catered for. Disturbance would be minimised

and the growth of suitable bankside vegetation and preservation of trees encouraged. As time went on the idea developed further with practical work being undertaken to 'improve' the habitat: stretches of bank were fenced from stock to allow scrub to develop; trees were planted and also thickets of scrub species; 'stick piles' were created from water-borne branches or tree trunks to provide lying-up places; in some areas artificial dens were built from drainpipes and bricks. In recent years, one company has even produced a flat-pack otter holt kit made of plastic which can easily be assembled on site.

Throughout the 1990s and into the new millennium, considerable sums of money were spent on this in an effort to assist in the recovery of the otter population. Many of the County Wildlife Trusts appointed Otter Officers who later evolved into Rivers and Otters Officers and then into Wetland Officers or similar, as they recognised that, while the otter is a useful 'flagship' species for attracting attention and funding, a more broadly-based approach made more sense in terms of practical conservation.

As we have learned more about otter ecology it has become clear that some of this work was not really necessary. The planting of trees beside rivers is a very good thing to do for all sorts of reasons but has no effect on otters – other than to provide places where, in the future, they will be able to deposit their spraints.

Looking back, it is interesting to see how much attention was paid to cleanliness (otters were supposed to be indicators of 'pristine' water conditions) and to the need to provide homes for otters in the form of artificial dens. In fact, we know that otters don't need artificial dens – they can quite easily find their own, even in the most unpromising environments and they don't mind mucky water either. Provided it doesn't poison them or their prey, water which looks distinctly unpleasant to us is readily exploited by otters without them coming to any harm.

Road deaths

The first indication that otter road casualties might have an impact on the population came from north Norfolk where, during the 1970s, five otters were killed in seven years at the place where the river Glaven flows under the road and into the sea. Two more were killed on roads within fifteen kilometres. This occurred at a time when the otter population was near its lowest in England and in fact, between the first and second surveys of England, the proportion of positive sites found in that area declined from sixteen per cent to one per cent. It is quite possible that the final extinction of otters in the area could have been brought about by these deaths.

With this in mind, during the 1980s some people made notes on otters killed on the roads, particularly in the south-west and began to collect the corpses where possible and submit them for examination. During the 1990s the numbers found began to increase and staff in the Environment Agency began to take an interest and encourage people to let them know when otters were found dead so that they could be collected and sent for post-mortem examination.

In Devon and Cornwall during the 1980s, thirty-two otter road casualties were recorded, averaging about three a year. In the first half of the 90s this increased to an average of fourteen a year, then to tenty-five until between 2001 and 2005 the rate was thirty-five per annum – a situation which was causing some concern. Part of this increase can be attributed to greater vigilance but the consistent increase also reflects changes in the otter population. South-west England has been a stronghold of otters since the very first English national survey when it was found that twnety-four per cent of the sites searched had signs of otters (more than half of all the positive sites found in England). In successive surveys this increased to forty-three per cent, sixty-seven per cent and eighty-three per cent. Today otters are found throughout Devon and Cornwall and it would seem that, despite the road mortality, the population has recovered over the whole area – otters are now found on every river and stream.

Otter populations in south-west England have clearly recovered despite this mortality but no-one wants to see otters killed when it can be avoided and there is also the possibility that in areas with a higher density of roads and traffic, such as the south-east, there could be a detrimental impact on the recovery. For these reasons, considerable efforts have been put into finding ways of reducing road mortality where it is feasible and cost effective to do so.

Sometimes otters are forced onto the roads, either because the river flowing beneath is permanently impassable to them, for example because a weir they cannot scale or a sluice gate forms a barrier, or because it is temporarily impassable, perhaps in spates when the water flows too fast for them to swim upstream. At other times they cross a road for no apparent reason and seem to have taken the decision to make a hazardous crossing over the road even though there is safe passage below. Geoff Liles calls these casualties 'enigmas'. Otters will also cross roads where there is no stream at all, for example when they want to cross the watershed from one catchment to another. A good example is the section of the A30 in Cornwall which runs along the watershed between the rivers Camel and Fowey where several have been killed, scattered over several kilometres of road.

Where there is a permanent barrier it is usually a good idea to create a safe way round it for otters. This might take the form of a cheap and effective remedy such as a simple ramp over a weir. Sometimes the only way to create a bypass is to put in a tunnel under the road, which is not too expensive when new roads are built but it is rarely feasible to install one retrospectively. Sometimes just putting up fencing to guide otters to a safe crossing and prevent them going over the road surface can be effective. Inside a culvert it may be possible to install a ledge which the otters can use when water levels are high and the current is too fast for them to swim upstream.

The Highways Agency has simple guidelines which have to be followed in the design and construction of new trunk roads and motorways and these can readily be applied to minor roads as well. I have been involved in the installation of quite a few ramps where, in the past, weirs were constructed in or beside culverts, thereby forcing otters on to the roads. The otters take to them readily, even leaving spraints on them, which helps to demonstrate that they are being used. At one site, four otters were killed in a period of twenty-eight months and one had been killed some six years earlier. Ramps were installed over two weirs which had been impassable and there have been no casualties since. At another, an otter spraint was deposited at the top of a ramp less than a week after it was installed – an expression of gratitude, I hope.

Pollution

When I left school (in my gap year – though they hadn't really been invented then) I worked for the Toxic Chemicals and Wildlife Division of the Nature Conservancy. The scientists working in that department were involved in studying the effects of toxic chemicals, particularly insecticides, on wildlife. It was their research which led to discoveries about the effect of eggshell thinning on populations of predatory birds. They demonstrated that large kills of seed-eating birds could be attributed to the use of insecticides and they teased out the subtle effects on the animals that preyed on them.

At the time I worked there, no-one realised that otters were being affected as well but they did know that populations of eagles, peregrines, sparrowhawks and many other species were suffering severely. It was the result of this work that led to the progressive withdrawal of these chemicals from use. One of the scientists I met there, Don Jefferies, subsequently went on to become the principal adviser on mammals to the Nature Conservancy Council and English Nature (successors to the Nature Conservancy) where he had a major influence on the course of otter conservation, including initiating the national otter surveys and our joint work on the otter hunting records.

Research on the impact of toxic chemicals on the environment continues, under the auspices of the Centre for Ecology and Hydrology, while the Environment Agency has taken responsibility for monitoring levels of these compounds, not only in the water but also in the wildlife that lives or feeds in it. We are much less likely to be caught unawares today than we were in the 1960s but the threats are still there.

Re-introduction

Another weapon in the conservationist's armoury is re-introduction. Seen by most people as a last resort it is still of potential benefit and it is of course important to make sure that, if it is done at all, it is done effectively. This is why, in the 1980s, the Nature Conservancy Council worked with the Otter Trust in carrying out a pilot re-introduction programme in East Anglia.

The otters were bred in captivity by the Otter Trust. Several were released in groups of three, one male plus two females, while others were released as pairs. When they were about 18 months old the groups were placed in a large, quiet enclosure away from public display. In due course they were taken to the site chosen for release and kept in a small enclosure for two or three weeks. Eventually a gate was opened and the otters were allowed to leave. Food was provided for the following twelve days, but less was put out each day. In some of the groups one animal, usually the male, was provided with a radio-transmitter which enabled the researchers to see how his home range developed. By the end of 1989, eighteen otters had been released in this way in East Anglia.

The programme did demonstrate the feasibility of releasing captive-bred otters and it was found that they tended to stay in the area selected for them. Within a matter of a few weeks they were using home ranges in a similar way to otters tracked on Scottish rivers. There is also indirect evidence that they have bred successfully and there is genetic evidence to suggest that the current otter population of East Anglia is substantially derived from these animals.

Having demonstrated that captive-born otters could be successfully released into the wild, the next question should be when and where this should be done. Many people felt very strongly that it should only be a last resort, perhaps to bolster a small and fragmented population, such as in East Anglia. Even then one has to question why the population is small and fragmented, there is little point in releasing captive bred animals unless they have a good chance of survival. However, there were others who felt that we didn't have time to waste but should go ahead and release otters where and when we could. As well as captive-bred otters, released mainly in eastern and southern England, some otters which had been re-habilitated were also released, mainly in Yorkshire. These were wild-born and had been found sick or injured, many as cubs, and were kept in captivity until they were thought fit and old enough to be released

Unfortunately, there was never a nationally agreed plan for re-introducing otters and many felt that the well-meaning attempts to do so were misplaced. Certainly the last major release of captive bred otters, in the upper Thames catchment, led to considerable controversy. Not least because of the presence of fish farms in the area.

There is no doubt that the recovery of the otter population in East Anglia, the Thames catchment and Yorkshire has been hastened by these releases. However, the natural recolonisation has also been very successful and, although it might have taken longer, there is little doubt that these areas would eventually have been recolonised naturally. Probably the main lesson to be learnt from this is that it is important for projects such as these to be carried out as part of a nationally-agreed program rather than simply through the enthusiasm of individuals or organisations.

Causes and effects

There is no doubt that the recovery of the otter is a success story for conservation in Britain. But what was it due to? Many people have put time, money and effort into otter conservation. Was it all worth it?

My own view is that, yes, it was worth it but probably not for the reasons it was done. In the early days of otter conservation we had little idea of what factors limited otter numbers in Britain and had to do what we thought was best at the time. Today we can be more confident that the food supply is the main limiting factor on otter numbers, combined with the time it will take for those numbers to recover as a result of breeding – in the wild. Lack of cover, clean water and dens or an excess of noise, disturbance or human activities has not stopped or even slowed the recovery. Pollution played the major role in the decline of the otter and equally the removal of sources of those pollutants has been the major factor in its return. The actions and decisions which led to the reduction of the pollutants responsible for the decline took place in the 1960s and 70s, not in the 1990s or later.

The activities involved in 'otter conservation' have had real practical benefits too. Much of the work that was done was beneficial – to birds, insects and many other species, if not to otters. They were also extremely good at getting people involved. My father took part in an otter holt building day and went on to create one on his own land. It may not have been a great step forward for the otter population (I don't think it has ever been used) but it certainly gained his interest and attention and led to a much greater awareness of the needs of wildlife as well as a recognition that he had a part to play in conservation. This was repeated many times over in the decade or more when the 'Save the Otter' campaign was running.

CURRENT THREATS

When the first edition of this book was published in 1993, only two national otter surveys had been carried out, and they showed that otters were largely confined to the south-west in England and still absent from a very high proportion of the country. The otter population seemed to be recovering very slowly and there was a widespread belief that, even though toxic chemicals had caused the initial decline, the recovery was being impeded by several factors. The Biodiversity Action Plan for Otters prepared in 1995 concluded that there were four 'factors causing loss or decline' of otters at that time – although we now know that by then the population was in fact recovering and increasing. These were: pollution of watercourses, especially by PCBs; insufficient prey associated with poor water quality; impoverished bankside habitat features needed for breeding and resting; incidental mortality, primarily by road deaths and drowning in eel traps. In the first edition of this book I discussed half a dozen factors under this heading (habitat destruction, disturbance, accidental deaths, toxic chemicals, population fragmentation, food supply) suggesting that some may be significant, though probably not all.

Now, twenty years on, it is clear that some of these concerns were misplaced (see below) and today we know that the otter population is recovering in much of the UK, indeed it has probably recovered to near pre-decline levels in some areas. The toxic chemicals which affected otters in the past continue to decline in the environment as well as in otters. We now know that otters are much more tolerant of human disturbance than we first thought and are also much less fussy about their habitat. There is no evidence that they need us to build artificial resting sites for them or to plant trees to 'improve' their habitat. Despite a considerable number of deaths on the roads in some places (notably south-west England) the population continues to thrive and to spread. So are there any current threats?

Inevitably, the answer is that we do not really know. We continue to invent wonderful new chemicals which seem essential to our survival, and then allow them to leak into the environment with unpredictable consequences. In recent years concern has been expressed about the impact of new chemicals used as flame retardants (PBDEs – polybrominated diphenyl ethers). We know that they occur in the aquatic environment, and in quite high concentrations in the tissues of otters but as yet we don't know if they are affecting otters or their prey.

We have also discovered that a range of 'endocrine disrupting compounds' have been causing profound changes in fish physiology so that in some rivers significant numbers of the male fish are 'feminised'. At present there is no evidence that otters are adversely affected but EDCs can lead to reduced fertility in fish. Should that be translated into reduced reproduction rates the consequences for the otter's food supply are obvious.

One new, but also very old threat to otters is from persecution. As numbers increase people begin to worry about the impact of otter predation on valuable, managed fish stocks. In practice, the legal protection afforded to otters ought to ensure that their status is not affected by any efforts to 'control' them, should these ever be allowed. In addition, illegal killing might have a local impact but is unlikely to cause the massive declines which have resulted from the impacts of toxic chemicals.

So, provided we don't poison them again or starve them by reducing their food supply, the otter population should continue to increase slowly until they are found in most of the places they lived in during the first half of the twentieth century by the middle of the twenty-first century. However, we cannot be complacent, and constant vigilance will be needed to ensure that neither of these things happen. Pollutants are now monitored systematically by the Environment Agency, which also monitors fish populations, so we are less likely to be taken unawares as we were in the past. It took more than ten years to be certain the otter population was declining in the 1960s, another twenty for us to work out why, and probably fifty more for the population to recover. Let us hope it never happens again.

Otters in literature

Many people were first introduced to the otter as Ratty's friend in *The Wind in the Willows*. I certainly was. The book was published in 1908 and, even today, Kenneth Graham's depiction of the otter as a loveable rogue strikes a chord with many people who have read it. Nineteen years later Henry Williamson published *Tarka the Otter*, a very different book. Far from writing about otters as if they were little people, Williamson tried to write a story about wild otters, based on his impression of their actual way of life. He described their daily lives and activities as active predators feeding on fish, frogs and rabbits and also recounted in some detail the deaths of otters as they were shot at, trapped and hunted by man.

Many admire Williamson as a writer but I must confess that I have never really enjoyed *Tarka* and it did not encourage me to read his other books. For those who do appreciate him, part of the appeal seems to lie in Williamson's descriptions of the North Devon countryside. If you know the area you can follow Tarka's travels very accurately because Williamson describes real places. I have even swum in the Junction Pool near Tarka's 'birthplace' (and found signs of real otter activity there as well).

Tarka has been recruited into the tourist industry with what was formerly British Rail naming their delightful route linking Barnstaple with Exeter as *The Tarka Line* and Devon County Council devising a *Tarka Trail*. The trail consists of a network of footpaths (some 180 miles of them) and cycle trails around the river valleys of the Taw and Torridge, along the North Devon coast and up onto the hills of Exmoor. All areas which 'Tarka' (i.e. Williamson) knew well.

However, the book that first brought otters to the attention of a wide audience was Gavin Maxwell's *Ring of Bright Water* published in 1960. I can still remember hearing extracts read from it, possibly on the radio, or at school. Over 100,000 copies of the book were sold in its first year of publication and it became a bestseller in America as well as in Britain. In 1962 a children's version, *The Otter's Tale*, was published and my own copy of this was my first introduction to 'real' otters. *Ring of Bright Water* was published as a Penguin paperback in 1974 and was eventually made into a film as well. It is still in print today. I have no doubt that its portrayal of otters as lovable, playful creatures influenced many people's views of this animal which, only a few years earlier, had been regarded as enough of a pest to warrant control by hunting.

Some people, particularly in the hunting fraternity, criticised the book saying that it persuaded many people that otters make suitable pets. They certainly come over as endearing animals but, if you read it carefully, you can see that they are also very demanding and cannot be kept in a conventional home.

Maxwell's two subsequent books, *The Rocks Remain* and *Raven Seek Thy Brother,* show how his apparently idyllic lifestyle on the west coast of Scotland came nearer to tragedy in subsequent years. Otters continued to feature largely in his life, despite the loss of Mijbil, his first otter, which strayed from home and was killed by a workman. These books reveal more fully the difficulties of keeping wild animals as pets. Even in his remote corner of Scotland with no neighbours Maxwell had to create zoo-like conditions to maintain his otters. He also discovered the unpredictability of wild creatures in captivity when two of his otters made serious attacks on people. The result of one of these was that his assistant had two fingers amputated. In the end Maxwell tried, unsuccessfully, to place the otters in suitable animal collections.

Maxwell's story is a complex and fascinating tale but one moral is clear – otters do not make good pets.

Since these classics there has been a dramatic increase in the number of books published, ranging from serious monographs by people such as Hans Kruuk, through more biographical works by authors like Philip Wayre, children's books and even a cookery book *(First, Peel the Otter: Grim and Ghastly Recipes for the Gruesome Gourmand* by John Henry Dixon). Several of the more serious ones are included in the *Further Reading* section and the Amazon website lists over 20,000 items under 'otter' if you care to search through them.

FURTHER READING

Some of the books below are out of print and may only be available from a library. However, a number are now available as 'print on demand' editions and more may become so with time.

Books

Otters: Ecology, Behaviour and Conservation by Hans Kruuk (Oxford University Press, 2006). This is the current, standard monograph on otters. It covers all species, discusses their biology and conservation and draws conclusions from comparisons between them.

Wild Otters: Predation and Populations by Hans Kruuk (Oxford University Press, 1995). An earlier book by Kruuk which focuses mainly on the research he and his colleagues carried out in Scotland.

The Natural History of Otters by Paul Chanin (Christopher Helm, 1984). Very out of date, an earlier monograph.

Otters: Ecology and Conservation by Chris Mason and Sheila Macdonald (Cambridge University Press, 2009). Somewhat dated. First published in 1986 and dealing with the Eurasian otter, it has a strong emphasis on conservation.

The Otter Among Us by James Williams (Tiercel Publishing, 2000). A personal account of otter natural history by a field naturalist with a great enthusiasm for the species.

The Otter by James Williams (Merlin Unwin Books, 2010). A more autobiographical account of otters with a great deal of information based on James's own observations and ideas.

Sea Otters by John Love (Whittet Books, 1990). An excellent account of a fascinating species.

A Guide to the Identification of Prey Remains in Otter Spraints by Jim Conroy, Jon Watt, Jean Webb and Anna Jones (The Mammal Society, 2005). A valuable guide to spraint analysis.

The Handbook of British Mammals (4th edition) edited by Derek Yalden and Stephen Harris (The Mammal Society, 2008). Everything you might want to know about British mammals and a lot more besides.

The Encyclopedia of Mammals (2nd edition) edited by David MacDonald (Oxford University Press, 2009). A lavishly illustrated tome describing the mammals of the world, including brief details of all the otter species.

Sources
The Mammal Society website (www.mammal.org.uk/) sells the Society's publications.

NHBS Environment Bookstore (www.nhbs.com/) seems to have every natural history book in the English language as well as many that aren't.

INDEX

The British Natural History Collection
Volume 1

OWLS

Chris Mead

Updated by Mike Toms &
illustrated by Guy Troughton

This updated classic reveals all sorts of
curious and unexpected facts about the
owls found in Britain, and also some
oddities about those species found elsewhere. Chris Mead, who was one of
Britain's foremost ornithologists, gives
readers helpful advice on how to observe
and count their local owls and how to assist
in protecting them.
This special edition features a gallery of full-colour photographs taken by Mark
Hancox, including his *BirdGuides* competition-winning photograph of a Short-
eared Owl.

*If you want to know anything about owls then this is the book for you ... This
Volume 1 is a must to start a valuable collection for the future.*
Ray Collier, Highland News

*The text lives up to the physical beauty of the book ... Maybe many people will
already know all of the many things which I learnt from this book, but perhaps
this book is aimed at people like me – people who appreciate wildlife without
knowing as much as we'd like – as much as real owl enthusiasts. With such a
beautiful book I expect it will be popular with all sorts of people.*
Rowan Adams, Naturenet

*If you are not currently an owl enthusiast you will be converted very quickly
once you have read this book.*
Bryan Sage, Country-Side (the magazine of the British Naturalists' Association)

Published by Whittet Books, ISBN 978 1 873580 83 7